THE ULTIMATE
SAN DIEGO PADRES
TRIVIA BOOK

A Collection of Amazing Trivia Quizzes
and Fun Facts for Die-Hard Pods Fans!

Ray Walker

Exclusive Free Book
Crazy Sports Stories

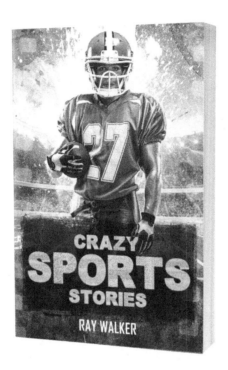

As a thank you for getting a copy of this book I would like to offer you a free copy of my book Crazy Sports Stories which comes packed with interesting stories from your favorite sports such as Football, Hockey, Baseball, Basketball and more.

Grab your free copy over at
RayWalkerMedia.com/Bonus

CONTENTS

Introduction 1

Chapter 1: Origins & History 3

    Quiz Time! 3

    Quiz Answers 8

    Did You Know? 9

Chapter 2: Jerseys & Numbers 11

    Quiz Time! 11

    Quiz Answers 16

    Did You Know? 17

Chapter 3: Mr. Padre 18

    Quiz Time! 18

    Quiz Answers 23

    Did You Know? 24

Chapter 4: Catchy Nicknames 26

    Quiz Time! 26

Quiz Answers...30

Did You Know?...31

Chapter 5: Trevor Time **32**

Quiz Time!...32

Quiz Answers...37

Did You Know?...38

Chapter 6: Statistically Speaking **40**

Quiz Time!...40

Quiz Answers...45

Did You Know?...46

Chapter 7: The Trade Market.....................................**48**

Quiz Time!...48

Quiz Answers...54

Did You Know?...55

Chapter 8: Draft Day...**57**

Quiz Time!...57

Quiz Answers...62

Did You Know?...63

Chapter 9: Odds & Ends...**64**

Quiz Time!...64

Quiz Answers 69

Did You Know? 70

Chapter 10: Outfielders..**71**

Quiz Time!.. 71

Quiz Answers 76

Did You Know? 77

Chapter 11: Infielders **80**

Quiz Time!.. 80

Quiz Answers 85

Did You Know? 86

Chapter 12: Pitchers and Catchers...........................**89**

Quiz Time!.. 89

Quiz Answers 94

Did You Know? 95

Chapter 13: World Series **98**

Quiz Time!.. 98

Quiz Answers 103

Did You Know? 104

Chapter 14: Heated Rivalries **106**

Quiz Time!.. 106

Quiz Answers..111

Did You Know?...112

Chapter 15: The Awards Section 115

Quiz Time!...115

Quiz Answers..120

Did You Know?...121

Chapter 16: America's Finest City 123

Quiz Time!...123

Quiz Answers..128

Did You Know?...129

Chapter 17: Winny..130

Quiz Time!...130

Quiz Answers..135

Did You Know?...136

Chapter 18: Peavy 137

Quiz Time!...137

Quiz Answers..142

Did You Know?...143

Chapter 19: America's Pastime 144

Quiz Time!...144

Quiz Answers 149

Did You Know? 150

Chapter 20: GOATs.. **152**

Quiz Time!.. 152

Quiz Answers 157

Did You Know? 158

Conclusion **161**

INTRODUCTION

The San Diego Padres were established in 1969 in San Diego, California. Throughout their more than 50 years of history, they have consistently proven themselves to be a team that fights hard and is a force to be reckoned with in MLB.

Though they have not yet won a World Series championship, they have a rich postseason history. They have won two National League pennants, five NL West Division titles, and a wild card berth. They are very often a threat in the National League West, having last won it in 2006.

The San Diego Padres have retired the uniform numbers of Tony Gwynn, Trevor Hoffman, Dave Winfield, Steve Garvey, and Randy Jones.

The team's current home is Petco Park, which opened in 2004. The Padres play in one of the most difficult divisions in baseball, the National League West, alongside the Los Angeles Dodgers, Colorado Rockies, San Francisco Giants, and Arizona Diamondbacks.

The thing about baseball is that it is a lot like life. There are good times and bad times, good days and bad days, but you have to do your absolute best to never give up. The San Diego

Padres have proven that they refuse to give up and that they will do anything they need to do to bring a championship to America's Finest City. Winning is more than possible when you have a legendary past like the San Diego Padres do. They have so much captivating history and so many undeniable player legacies to be profoundly proud of.

With such a storied team past, you're probably already very knowledgeable as the die-hard Padres fan that you are. Let's test that knowledge to see if you truly are the world's biggest San Diego Padres fan.

The stats presented in this book are current as of the end of the 2020 MLB season.

CHAPTER 1:

ORIGINS & HISTORY

QUIZ TIME!

1. Which of the following team names did the San Diego Padres franchise once go by?

    a. San Diego Aztecs

    b. San Diego Chickens

    c. San Diego Surfers

    d. They have always been the Padres.

2. In what year was the San Diego Padres franchise established?

    a. 1968

    b. 1969

    c. 1978

    d. 1979

3. The San Diego Padres' current home stadium is Petco Park.

    a. True

    b. False

4. Which division do the San Diego Padres play in?

    a. American League West
    b. National League West
    c. American League Central
    d. National League Central

5. The San Diego Padres have never won a wild card berth.

    a. True
    b. False

6. How many National League pennants have the San Diego Padres won?

    a. 0
    b. 1
    c. 2
    d. 3

7. Who is the current principal owner of the San Diego Padres?

    a. Larry Dolan
    b. Robert Nutting
    c. Arturo Moreno
    d. Peter Seidler

8. Who is the winningest manager in franchise history?

    a. Bud Black
    b. Dick Williams
    c. Bruce Bochy
    d. Don Zimmer

9. What is the name of the San Diego Padres Triple-A team and where is it located?

   a. Albuquerque Isotopes
   b. Jacksonville Jumbo Shrimp
   c. Toledo Mud Hens
   d. El Paso Chihuahuas

10. Who was the first manager of the franchise?

    a. Don Zimmer
    b. Preston Gómez
    c. John McNamara
    d. Dick Williams

11. The San Diego Padres were members of the American League West from 1969 through 1998.

    a. True
    b. False

12. What is the name of the San Diego Padres' spring training home stadium?

    a. Peoria Sports Complex
    b. Hohokam Stadium
    c. Salt River Fields
    d. Sloan Park

13. How many appearances has the franchise made in the MLB playoffs?

    a. 2
    b. 4

c. 6

d. 8

14. How many World Series titles have the San Diego Padres won?

    a. 0

    b. 1

    c. 2

    d. 3

15. San Diego's current manager is Jayce Tingler.

    a. True

    b. False

16. What was the franchise's first home stadium?

    a. Chargers Stadium

    b. Petco Park

    c. Qualcomm Stadium

    d. Tony Gwynn Stadium

17. Who is the current general manager of the San Diego Padres?

    a. Mike Rizzo

    b. A.J. Preller

    c. David Forst

    d. Jerry Dipoto

18. How many National League West Division titles have the San Diego Padres won?

    a. 3

    b. 5

c. 7

d. 10

19. A.J. Preller is the current president of baseball operations for the San Diego Padres.

   a. True

   b. False

20. The San Diego Padres are the only current MLB team that does not have an NFL team in its city.

   a. True

   b. False

QUIZ ANSWERS

1. D – They have always been the Padres.

2. B – 1969

3. A – True

4. B – National League West

5. B – False (2020)

6. C – 2

7. D – Peter Seidler

8. C – Bruce Bochy

9. D – El Paso Chihuahuas

10. B – Preston Gómez

11. B – False (they have always been in the NL West.)

12. A – Peoria Sports Complex

13. C – 6

14. A – 0

15. A – True

16. C – Qualcomm Stadium

17. B – A.J. Preller

18. B – 5

19. A – True

20. B – False (Blue Jays, Brewers, Cardinals, Athletics, and Padres)

DID YOU KNOW?

1. The San Diego Padres have had 21 managers so far. They are Preston Gómez, Don Zimmer, John McNamara, Bob Skinner, Alvin Dark, Roger Craig, Jerry Coleman, Frank Howard, Dick Williams, Steve Boros, Larry Bowa, Jack McKeon, Greg Riddoch, Jim Riggleman, Bruce Bochy, Bud Black, Dave Roberts, Pat Murphy, Andy Green, Rod Barajas, and Jayce Tingler.

2. San Diego's current manager is Jayce Tingler, who has been their manager since 2020. He played minor league baseball for four seasons after being drafted by the Toronto Blue Jays in the 10th round of the 2003 MLB draft. He coached and was an assistant general manager for the Texas Rangers from 2015 to 2016 and 2018 to 2019.

3. Bruce Bochy is the San Diego Padres' all-time winningest manager with a record of 951-975 for a .494 winning percentage. Bochy managed the Padres from 1995 to 2006. Bochy is a former MLB catcher who spent his MLB career with the Houston Astros, New York Mets, and Padres. He was the manager of the San Francisco Giants from 2007 to 2019.

4. The San Diego Padres and the Los Angeles Angels are the only two California teams that originated in the state of California.

5. San Diego Padres has hosted three All-Star Games so: 1978 at San Diego Stadium, 1992 at Jack Murphy Stadium, and 2016 at Petco Park.

6. No San Diego pitcher has thrown a no-hitter through the end of the 2020 season.

7. The name "Padres" means "Fathers" in Spanish. The Padres are named after the Spanish Franciscan friars who founded San Diego in 1769.

8. The San Diego Padres' Double-A team is the San Antonio Missions, their High Single-A team is the Fort Wayne TinCaps, and their Low Single-A team is the Lake Elsinore Storm.

9. San Diego's current mascot is the Swinging Friar. He has been the mascot of the team since the Padres were in the Pacific Coast League. He is cartoon-like, balding, and chubby. He wears sandals, a cloak, and rope around his waist. He is often seen swinging a baseball bat.

10. The San Diego Padres have retired five numbers so far (six including Jackie Robinson's No. 42, which is retired league-wide). The numbers retired are Tony Gwynn's No. 19, Steve Garvey's No. 6, Dave Winfield's No. 31, Randy Jones' No. 35, and Trevor Hoffman's No. 51.

CHAPTER 2:

JERSEYS & NUMBERS

QUIZ TIME!

1. The team's original colors were brown and gold.

    a. True
    b. False

2. What are the San Diego Padres' current official team colors?

    a. Brown, gold, and orange
    b. Brown, gold, and white
    c. Blue, orange, and sand
    d. Blue, white, and gold

3. In 2000, the San Diego Padres began wearing camouflage jerseys to honor the U.S. military.

    a. True
    b. False

4. Which of the following numbers has NOT been retired by the San Diego Padres?

a. 19
b. 31
c. 36
d. 51

5. What number does Fernando Tatis Jr. currently wear?

   a. 3
   b. 10
   c. 13
   d. 23

6. What number did Tony Gwynn wear during his time with the San Diego Padres?

   a. 9
   b. 19
   c. 29
   d. 39

7. Trevor Hoffman wore the Nos. 51 and 34 during his time with the San Diego Padres.

   a. True
   b. False

8. What number did Dave Winfield wear during his time with the San Diego Padres?

   a. 21
   b. 30
   c. 31
   d. 32

9. What number does Manny Machado currently wear?

   a. 8
   b. 10
   c. 13
   d. 15

10. No San Diego Padres player has ever worn No. 0.

   a. True
   b. False

11. What number did Jake Peavy wear as a member of the San Diego Padres?

   a. 11
   b. 22
   c. 33
   d. 44

12. What number did Adrian Gonzalez wear as a member of the San Diego Padres?

   a. 21
   b. 23
   c. 24
   d. 28

13. Andy Ashby wore the No. 43 during his time with the San Diego Padres.

   a. True
   b. False

14. What number did Andy Benes wear as a member of the San Diego Padres?

a. 20

b. 30

c. 40

d. Both B and C

15. What number did Randy Jones wear as a member of the San Diego Padres?

   a. 25

   b. 30

   c. 35

   d. None of the above

16. What number does Eric Hosmer currently wear as a member of the San Diego Padres?

   a. 3

   b. 10

   c. 20

   d. 30

17. What number does Wil Myers currently wear as a member of the San Diego Padres?

   a. 4

   b. 5

   c. 8

   d. 9

18. What number did Gene Tenace wear with the San Diego Padres?

   a. 18

   b. 24

c. 38

d. 45

19. What number did Chase Headley wear as a member of the San Diego Padres?

    a. 7

    b. 12

    c. 16

    d. All of the above

20. Phil Nevin wore the No. 23 during his time with the San Diego Padres.

    a. True

    b. False

QUIZ ANSWERS

1. A - True

2. B – Brown, gold, and white

3. A – True

4. C – 36

5. D – 23

6. B – 19

7. A – True

8. C – 31

9. C – 13

10. B – False (Rafael Lopez)

11. D – 44

12. B – 23

13. A – True

14. C – 40

15. C – 35

16. D – 30

17. A – 4

18. A – 18

19. D – All of the above

20. A – True

DID YOU KNOW?

1. The San Diego Padres have retired six uniform numbers overall so far: Steve Garvey's No. 6, Tony Gwynn's No. 19, Dave Winfield's No. 31, Randy Jones' No. 35, Trevor Hoffman's No. 51, and Jackie Robinson's No. 42.

2. During his time with the San Diego Padres, Gene Richards wore Nos. 9, 17, 19, and 29.

3. During his time with the San Diego Padres, Brian Giles wore No. 24.

4. During his time with the San Diego Padres, Nate Colbert wore No. 17.

5. During his time with the San Diego Padres, Terry Kennedy wore No. 16.

6. During his time with the San Diego Padres, Eric Show wore the uniform numbers 30 and 44.

7. Jackie Robinson's No. 42 has been retired MLB as a whole. No Padres or MLB player will ever wear No. 42 again. The Yankees' Mariano Rivera was the last player to wear it.

8. During his time with the San Diego Padres, Ed Whitson wore Nos. 31, 32, and 38.

9. During his time with the San Diego Padres, Ryan Klesko wore No. 30.

10. During his time with the San Diego Padres, Will Venable wore No. 25.

CHAPTER 3:

MR. PADRE

QUIZ TIME!

1. What is Tony Gwynn's full name?

    a. James Anthony Gwynn

    b. Anthony James Gwynn

    c. Anthony Keith Gwynn

    d. Keith Anthony Gwynn

2. Tony Gwynn played his entire 20-season MLB career with the San Diego Padres.

    a. True

    b. False

3. Where was Tony Gwynn born?

    a. Poway, California

    b. Los Angeles, California

    c. San Diego, California

    d. Long Beach, California

4. When was Tony Gwynn born?

a. March 9, 1960

b. March 9, 1969

c. May 9, 1960

d. May 9, 1969

5. Tony Gwynn won the Roberto Clemente Award in 1999.

a. True

b. False

6. How many All-Star Games was Tony Gwynn named to during his 20-season MLB career?

a. 9

b. 10

c. 12

d. 15

7. What year was Tony Gwynn inducted into the National Baseball Hall of Fame with 97.6% of the vote?

a. 2005

b. 2007

c. 2009

d. 2012

8. Tony Gwynn attended college at San Diego State University.

a. True

b. False

9. How many National League batting titles did Tony Gwynn win?

a. 2

b. 4

c. 6

d. 8

10. What year did Tony Gwynn make his MLB debut?

a. 1980

b. 1981

c. 1982

d. 1983

11. How many Gold Glove Awards did Tony Gwynn win in his 20-season MLB career?

a. 3

b. 5

c. 7

d. 9

12. Tony Gwynn's son, Tony Gwynn Jr., played for the San Diego Padres in 2009 and 2010.

a. True

b. False

13. How many Silver Slugger Awards did Tony Gwynn win?

a. 4

b. 5

c. 7

d. 10

14. There is a statue of Tony Gwynn behind right center field at Petco Park.

a. True

b. False

15. How many home runs did Tony Gwynn hit?

   a. 115
   b. 125
   c. 135
   d. 145

16. How many bases did Tony Gwynn steal?

   a. 309
   b. 319
   c. 329
   d. 339

17. Tony Gwynn played in both of the San Diego Padres' only two World Series appearances to date.

   a. True
   b. False

18. How many hits did Tony Gwynn collect?

   a. 2,841
   b. 2,941
   c. 3,041
   d. 3,141

19. At San Diego State University, Tony Gwynn played baseball and which other sport?

   a. Soccer
   b. Basketball
   c. Football
   d. Golf

20. San Diego State's baseball stadium is called Tony Gwynn Stadium.

    a. True
    b. False

QUIZ ANSWERS

1. C – Anthony Keith Gwynn

2. A – True

3. B – Los Angeles, California

4. C – May 9, 1960

5. A – True

6. D – 15

7. B – 2007

8. A – True

9. D – 8

10. C – 1982

11. B – 5

12. A – True

13. C – 7

14. A – True

15. C – 135

16. B – 319

17. A - True

18. D – 3,141

19. B – Basketball

20. A – True

DID YOU KNOW?

1. Tony Gwynn often accepted less money to remain with the small-market Padres.

2. After retiring from MLB, Tony Gwynn became the head coach of his alma mater's baseball team at San Diego State University. His mantra for his players was "Do things right." He was the Aztecs' head coach for 12 seasons until his death.

3. Tony Gwynn passed away in 2014 due to complications from parotid cancer. He believed his cancer diagnosis was due to his heavy use of chewing tobacco since 1981. More than 23,000 fans attended a public memorial service for Mr. Padre at Petco Park. In 2018, Gwynn's family reached a settlement with the U.S. Smokeless Tobacco Company after filing a wrongful death lawsuit.

4. Tony Gwynn's daughter, Anisha Nicole, is an R&B singer. Tony Gwynn Jr. spent eight years in MLB, two of those seasons with the Padres. Tony's brother, Chris Gwynn, also played in MLB for 10 seasons, one of those seasons with the Padres.

5. Tony Gwynn was not allowed to play baseball his freshman season at SDSU due to being overweight at 205 pounds. He played three seasons of baseball and four seasons of basketball in his collegiate career.

6. After Tony Gwynn's death, the Mountain West Conference renamed its Player of the Year Award as the Tony Gwynn Award. In 2016, MLB announced the National League batting title would be renamed in Gwynn's honor.

7. Tony Gwynn's Hall of Fame voting percentage of 97.61% is the 10th highest voting percentage in voting history.

8. Former MLB commissioner Bud Selig called Tony Gwynn "the greatest Padre ever and one of the most accomplished hitters that our game has ever known, whose all-around excellence on the field was surpassed by his exuberant personality and genial disposition in life."

9. Tony Gwynn was the head coach of the SDSU baseball team during Stephen Strasburg's time playing for the Aztecs. He was a mentor for Strasburg, the 2009 Washington Nationals' No. 1 MLB draft pick.

10. Tony Gwynn played in 2,440 MLB games with the Padres. He collected 1,138 RBIs and had a career batting average of .338.

CHAPTER 4:

CATCHY NICKNAMES

QUIZ TIME!

1. What nickname does Fernando Tatis Jr. go by?

    a. El Rey

    b. El Fuerte

    c. El Niño

    d. El Rapido

2. Tony Gwynn went by the nickname "Mr. Padre."

    a. True

    b. False

3. What nickname does Dave Winfield go by?

    a. Big Dave

    b. Fieldy

    c. Big Win

    d. Winny

4. What nickname does Adrian Gonzalez go by?

    a. El Hombre

    b. El Titan

c. El Mejor

d. El Grande

5. What nickname does Andy Benes go by?

   a. Thunder Storm

   b. Sandy Andy

   c. Baked Benes

   d. Rain Man

6. Which nickname does Gene Tenace go by?

   a. School Bus

   b. Tenace Train

   c. Steamboat

   d. Big G

7. Chase Headley goes by the simple nickname "Head."

   a. True

   b. False

8. What nickname does Ozzie Smith go by?

   a. Backflip

   b. The Wizard of Oz

   c. Tiger

   d. Cartwheel

9. What nickname does Fernando Valenzuela go by?

   a. El Escorpion

   b. El León

   c. El Rey

   d. El Toro

10. What nickname does Wally Joyner go by?

    a. The Wall
    b. California Wallace
    c. Wally World
    d. Jump for Joy

11. What nickname does Rickey Henderson go by?

    a. The Man of Steal
    b. Son of Steal
    c. Running Rickey
    d. Hendo

12. Phil Nevin goes by the simple nickname "Nev."

    a. True
    b. False

13. What nickname does Eric Hosmer go by?

    a. Fast Hands
    b. Hammer
    c. Hoz
    d. Homerin' Hosmer

14. What nickname does Manny Machado go by?

    a. Hakuna Machado
    b. Mr. Miami
    c. El Ministro de Defensa
    d. All of the above

15. Wil Myers goes by the nickname "El Gallo."

    a. True
    b. False

16. What nickname was given to the moments when Trevor Hoffman entered the field in San Diego?

   a. Hoffy's Hour
   b. K Corral
   c. Trevor Time
   d. Bedtime

17. Gary Sheffield goes by the nickname "Sheff."

   a. True
   b. False

18. "Bip" is a nickname. What is Bip Roberts' full name?

   a. David Bartholomew Roberts
   b. Bartholomew David Roberts
   c. Joseph Leon Roberts
   d. Leon Joseph Roberts

19. "Rollie" is a nickname. What is Rollie Fingers' full name?

   a. Glen Roland Fingers
   b. Roland Glen Fingers
   c. Ronald Ray Fingers
   d. Ray Ronald Fingers

20. Justin Upton goes by the nickname "J-Up."

   a. True
   b. False

QUIZ ANSWERS

1. C – El Niño

2. A – True

3. D – Winny

4. B – El Titan

5. D – Rain Man

6. C – Steamboat

7. A – True

8. B – The Wizard of Oz

9. D – El Toro

10. C – Wally World

11. A – The Man of Steal

12. A – True

13. C – Hoz

14. D – All of the above

15. A - True

16. C – Trevor Time

17. A – True

18. D – Leon Joseph Roberts

19. B – Roland Glen Fingers

20. A – True

DID YOU KNOW?

1. Benito Santiago goes by the nickname "Benny."

2. Former Padres manager Bruce Bochy goes by the simple nickname "Boch."

3. "Bud" is a nickname. Former Padres manager Bud Black's full name is Harry Ralston Black.

4. "Goose" is a nickname. Goose Gossage's full name is Richard Michael Gossage.

5. Dave Roberts goes by the nickname "Doc."

6. Austin Hedges goes by the nickname "Hedgey."

7. Doug Rader goes by the nicknames, "Rojo" and "Red Rooster."

8. Fred McGriff goes by the nickname "Crime Dog."

9. Garry Templeton goes by the nickname "Jumpsteady."

10. Graig Nettles goes by the nickname "Puff."

CHAPTER 5:

TREVOR TIME

QUIZ TIME!

1. What is Trevor Hoffman's full name?

   a. William Trevor Hoffman

   b. Trevor William Hoffman

   c. Trevor Michael Hoffman

   d. Michael Trevor Hoffman

2. Trevor Hoffman played his entire 18-season MLB career with the San Diego Padres.

   a. True

   b. False

3. Where was Trevor Hoffman born?

   a. Phoenix, Arizona

   b. Tucson, Arizona

   c. Anaheim, California

   d. Bellflower, California

4. When was Trevor Hoffman born?

a. October 13, 1977

b. October 13, 1967

c. September 13, 1977

d. September 13, 1967

5. Trevor Hoffman did NOT win a World Series championship during his 18-season MLB career.

a. True

b. False

6. How many All-Star Games was Trevor Hoffman named to?

a. 2

b. 4

c. 5

d. 7

7. How many Rolaids Relief Man of the Year Awards did Trevor Hoffman win?

a. 1

b. 2

c. 3

d. 4

8. The street in front of the Padres' offices at Petco Park was renamed Trevor Hoffman Way in 2018.

a. True

b. False

9. What year was Trevor Hoffman inducted into the National Baseball Hall of Fame?

    a. 2016
    b. 2017
    c. 2018
    d. 2019

10. How many seasons did Trevor Hoffman lead the National League in saves?

    a. 0
    b. 1
    c. 2
    d. 3

11. How many saves did Trevor Hoffman collect?

    a. 401
    b. 501
    c. 601
    d. 701

12. Trevor Hoffman is currently the senior adviser of baseball operations for the San Diego Padres.

    a. True
    b. False

13. Which AC/DC song did Trevor Hoffman use as his walk-out song during home games at Petco Park?

    a. Highway to Hell
    b. Hells Bells

c. It's a Long Way to the Top

d. Back in Black

14. Trevor Hoffman is in the San Diego Padres Hall of Fame and the Milwaukee Brewers Wall of Honor.

a. True

b. False

15. What is Trevor Hoffman's career ERA?

a. 2.77

b. 2.87

c. 2.97

d. 3.07

16. How many strikeouts did Trevor Hoffman record?

a. 1,133

b. 1,233

c. 1,333

d. 1,533

17. Trevor Hoffman retired with the highest career strikeout rate of any reliever in MLB history.

a. True

b. False

18. How many times did Trevor Hoffman win *The Sporting News* Reliever of the Year Award?

a. 1

b. 2

c. 3

d. 4

19. When Trevor Hoffman met his wife, Tracy, she was a cheerleader for which professional sports franchise?

    a. San Diego Chargers
    b. Buffalo Bills
    c. Los Angeles Lakers
    d. New York Knicks

20. Trevor Hoffman was the first MLB player to reach both 500 and 600 saves.

    a. True
    b. False

QUIZ ANSWERS

1. B – Trevor William Hoffman

2. B – False (He pitched for the Padres, Brewers, and Marlins.)

3. D – Bellflower, California

4. B – October 13, 1967

5. A – True

6. D – 7

7. B – 2

8. A – True

9. C – 2018

10. C – 2

11. C – 601

12. A – True

13. B – Hells Bells

14. A – True

15. B – 2.87

16. A – 1,133

17. A – True

18. C – 3 (1996, 1998, 2006)

19. B – Buffalo Bills

20. A – True

DID YOU KNOW?

1. In 2014, MLB announced the establishment of the Trevor Hoffman National League Reliever of the Year Award. The award is given each year to the top reliever in the NL.

2. Trevor Hoffman asked his wife Tracy to marry him while she was on the field for Super Bowl XXVII.

3. Trevor Hoffman donated $200 to the National Kidney Foundation for each save that he recorded.

4. In honor of his father, who was a Marine, Trevor Hoffman bought game tickets and meals for 1,000 members of the military and their families each season.

5. Trevor Hoffman holds the MLB record for most National League career saves with 601.

6. Trevor Hoffman was named the National League Pitcher of the Month in May 2005 and May 2009.

7. Trevor Hoffman holds the MLB record for most career games pitched with one team at 902 during his 16 seasons with the Padres.

8. There is a bronze statue of Trevor Hoffman near the bullpens at Petco Park.

9. At the University of Arizona, Trevor Hoffman played alongside teammates including J.T. Snow, Scott Erickson, and Kevin Long.

10. Trevor Hoffman was the bullpen coach for the Great Britain team in the 2017 World Baseball Classic. He was eligible due to his English roots on his mother's side.

CHAPTER 6:

STATISTICALLY SPEAKING

QUIZ TIME!

1. Nate Colbert holds the San Diego franchise record for the most home runs. How many home runs did he hit while with his Padres?

   a. 156
   b. 161
   c. 163
   d. 183

2. Pitcher Eric Show has the most wins in franchise history with 100.

   a. True
   b. False

3. Which pitcher holds the San Diego record for most career shutouts thrown with 18?

   a. Bruce Hurst
   b. Eric Show
   c. Steve Arlin
   d. Randy Jones

4. Which San Diego batter holds the team's single-season record for strikeouts with 180?

   a. Justin Upton
   b. Mike Cameron
   c. Wil Myers
   d. Eric Hosmer

5. Pitcher Jake Peavy has the most strikeouts in San Diego Padres franchise history with how many?

   a. 1,029
   b. 1,036
   c. 1,348
   d. 1,582

6. Tony Gwynn has the most stolen bases in franchise history with how many?

   a. 148
   b. 171
   c. 242
   d. 319

7. Trevor Hoffman holds the record for most saves in San Diego Padres history with 552.

   a. True
   b. False

8. Who holds the San Diego Padres record for being intentionally walked with 203?

   a. Adrian Gonzalez
   b. Tony Gwynn

c. Dave Winfield

d. Garry Templeton

9. Which player holds the San Diego Padres franchise record for home runs in a single season with 50?

a. Greg Vaughn

b. Phil Nevin

c. Ken Caminiti

d. Adrian Gonzalez

10. Which batter holds the single-season San Diego Padres record for hits with 220?

a. Gene Richards

b. Steve Finley

c. Mark Loretta

d. Tony Gwynn

11. Who holds the San Diego record for double plays grounded into in a single season with 25?

a. Benito Santiago

b. Steve Garvey

c. Kevin Kouzmanoff

d. Both B and C

12. Tony Gwynn holds the record for the most sacrifice flies in franchise history with 85.

a. True

b. False

13. Clay Kirby threw the most wild pitches in San Diego franchise history with how many?

a. 40

b. 42

c. 48

d. 50

14. Tony Gwynn and Dave Roberts are tied for the team's single-season record for triples. How many did they each hit (Gwynn in 1987, Roberts in 2006)?

a. 10

b. 11

c. 12

d. 13

15. Which hitter has the most walks in San Diego Padres franchise history with 790?

a. Brian Giles

b. Tony Gwynn

c. Ryan Klesko

d. Dave Winfield

16. Which San Diego Padres hitter holds the all-time franchise record for batting average at .338?

a. Dave Winfield

b. Bip Roberts

c. Mark Loretta

d. Tony Gwynn

17. Tony Gwynn holds the franchise record for most runs scored with 1,383.

a. True

b. False

18. Tony Gwynn has the most plate appearances in franchise history with how many?

    a. 8,232
    b. 9,232
    c. 10,232
    d. 11,232

19. Which pitcher holds the San Diego franchise record for most saves in a single season with 53?

    a. Heath Bell
    b. Trevor Hoffman
    c. Mark Davis
    d. Rollie Fingers

20. Randy Jones holds the franchise record for most losses by a pitcher with 105.

    a. True
    b. False

QUIZ ANSWERS

1. C – 163

2. A - True

3. D – Randy Jones

4. C – Wil Myers (2017)

5. C – 1,348

6. D – 319

7. A – True

8. B – Tony Gwynn

9. A – Greg Vaughn (1998)

10. D – Tony Gwynn (1997)

11. D – Both B and C (Garvey 1984 and 1985, Kouzmanoff 2009)

12. A – True

13. C – 48

14. D – 13

15. B – Tony Gwynn

16. D – Tony Gwynn

17. A – True

18. C – 10,232

19. B – Trevor Hoffman (1998)

20. A – True

DID YOU KNOW?

1. Randy Jones threw the most innings in San Diego franchise history with 1,766.0. Coming in second is Eric Show, who threw 1,603.1 innings.

2. Tony Gwynn had the best single-season batting average in franchise history at .394 in 1994. Coming in second is Tony Gwynn again with a .372 batting average in 1997.

3. Will Venable holds the San franchise record for stolen base percentage with 80.75% success. Tony Gwynn holds the franchise record for stolen bases with 319. Gwynn also holds the franchise record for the most times caught stealing at 125.

4. Tony Gwynn has the most extra base hits in franchise history with 763. Second on the list is Dave Winfield with 372.

5. Fred McGriff holds the San Diego record for at-bats per home run at 16.2. This means McGriff hit a home run about every 16 to 17 at-bats.

6. Trevor Hoffman holds the franchise record for strikeouts per nine innings pitched at 9.725. This means that, during his time with the Padres, Hoffman recorded nearly 10 strikeouts for every nine innings he pitched.

7. Chase Headley holds the San Diego record for the most hit by pitches with 38. Joey Hamilton and Eric Show are tied for the team record for most batters hit with 46 each.

8. Tony Gwynn holds the franchise record for career doubles with 543. Second on the list is Garry Templeton with 195.

9. Randy Jones holds San Diego's single-season record for wins with 22 in 1976. He also holds the San Diego Padres single-season record for most losses with 22 in 1974.

10. Wil Myers holds the franchise record for most strikeouts in a single season with 180 in 2017. Kevin Brown holds the franchise record for most strikeouts thrown in a single season with 257 in 1998.

CHAPTER 7:

THE TRADE MARKET

QUIZ TIME!

1. On February 2, 1999, the San Diego Padres traded Greg Vaughn and Mark Sweeney to which team in exchange for Reggie Sanders, Damian Jackson, and Josh Harris?

   a. Milwaukee Brewers

   b. Cincinnati Reds

   c. Tampa Bay Devil Rays

   d. Colorado Rockies

2. On July 31, 2009, the San Diego Padres traded Jake Peavy to which team in exchange for Aaron Poreda, Clayton Richard, Adam Russell, and Dexter Carter?

   a. Toronto Blue Jays

   b. Boston Red Sox

   c. San Francisco Giants

   d. Chicago White Sox

3. The San Diego Padres have made only four trades with the Los Angeles Dodgers.

a. True

b. False

4. On June 20, 1998, the San Diego Padres traded Carlos Reyes, Mandy Romero, and Dario Veras to which team in exchange for Jim Leyritz and Ethan Faggett?

   a. Boston Red Sox
   b. New York Yankees
   c. Boston Red Sox
   d. Texas Rangers

5. The San Diego Padres have made 12 trades with the Tampa Bay Rays.

   a. True
   b. False

6. On June 24, 1993, the San Diego Padres traded Gary Sheffield and Rich Rodriguez to which team in exchange for Trevor Hoffman, Jose Martinez, and Andrés Berumen?

   a. Los Angeles Dodgers
   b. New York Yankees
   c. Florida Marlins
   d. Milwaukee Brewers

7. On December 28, 1994, the San Diego Padres traded Derek Bell, Doug Brocail, Pedro Martinez, Ricky Gutierrez, Phil Plantier, and Craig Shipley to which team in exchange for Steve Finley, Ken Caminiti, Brian Williams, Andújar Cedeño, Roberto Petagine, and a player to be named later (Sean Fesh)?

a. Arizona Diamondbacks

b. Houston Astros

c. Baltimore Orioles

d. California Angels

8. On January 6, 2006, the San Diego Padres traded Adam Eaton, Akinori Otsuka, and Billy Killian to which team in exchange for Adrian Gonzalez, Chris Young, and Terrmel Sledge?

a. Los Angeles Dodgers

b. Oakland A's

c. Boston Red Sox

d. Texas Rangers

9. On April 5, 2015, the Padres traded Cameron Maybin, Carlos Quentin, Matt Wisler, Jordan Paroubeck, and a 2015 competitive balance Round A pick to which team for B.J. Upton and Craig Kimbrel?

a. Chicago Cubs

b. Tampa Bay Rays

c. Atlanta Braves

d. Boston Red Sox

10. The San Diego Padres have made only four trades with the Arizona Diamondbacks.

a. True

b. False

11. On July 26, 1993, the San Diego Padres traded Greg Harris and Bruce Hurst to which team in exchange for Brad

Ausmus, Doug Bochtler, and a player to be named later (Andy Ashby)?

a. Detroit Tigers
b. Houston Astros
c. Minnesota Twins
d. Colorado Rockies

12. The San Diego Padres have made six trades with the Colorado Rockies.

a. True
b. False

13. On December 17, 2011, the San Diego Padres traded Mat Latos to the which team in exchange for Yonder Alonso, Yasmani Grandal, Brad Boxberger, and Edinson Vólquez?

a. Cincinnati Reds
b. Oakland A's
c. Chicago White Sox
d. Los Angeles Dodgers

14. The San Diego Padres have made seven trades with the Florida/Miami Marlins.

a. True
b. False

15. On January 6, 2012, the San Diego Padres traded Zach Cates and which player to the Chicago Cubs in exchange for Andrew Cashner and Kyung-Min Na?

a. Kyle Schwarber
b. Javier Baez

c. Anthony Rizzo

d. Kris Bryant

16. On December 6, 1996, the San Diego Padres traded Scott Sanders to which team in exchange for Sterling Hitchcock?

   a. Detroit Tigers

   b. Seattle Mariners

   c. New York Yankees

   d. St. Louis Cardinals

17. On July 31, 2011, the San Diego Padres traded Mike Adams to which team in exchange for Joe Wieland and Robbie Erlin?

   a. Texas Rangers

   b. Philadelphia Phillies

   c. Milwaukee Brewers

   d. Pittsburgh Pirates

18. On December 5, 1990, the San Diego Padres traded Roberto Alomar and Joe Carter to which team in exchange for Fred McGriff and Tony Fernández?

   a. Tampa Bay Devil Rays

   b. Atlanta Braves

   c. Cleveland Indians

   d. Toronto Blue Jays

19. On December 10, 1981, the San Diego Padres traded Ozzie Smith, Steve Mura, and a player to be named later (Al Olmsted) to which team in exchange for Sixto Lezcano,

Garry Templeton, and a player to be named later (Luis DeLeón)?

a. Milwaukee Brewers
b. Philadelphia Phillies
c. St. Louis Cardinals
d. Pittsburgh Pirates

20. The San Diego Padres have made 11 trades with the San Francisco Giants.

a. True
b. False

QUIZ ANSWERS

1. B – Cincinnati Reds

2. D – Chicago White Sox

3. A – True

4. A – Boston Red Sox

5. A – True

6. C – Florida Marlins

7. B – Houston Astros

8. D – Texas Rangers

9. C – Atlanta Braves

10. A – True

11. D – Colorado Rockies

12. A – True

13. A – Cincinnati Reds

14. B – False (17)

15. C – Anthony Rizzo

16. B – Seattle Mariners

17. A – Texas Rangers

18. D – Toronto Blue Jays

19. C – St. Louis Cardinals

20. A – True

DID YOU KNOW?

1. On December 15, 1997, the San Diego Padres traded Derrek Lee, Steve Hoff, and Rafael Medina to the Florida Marlins in exchange for Kevin Brown.

2. On June 4, 2016, the San Diego Padres traded James Shields and cash considerations to the Chicago White Sox in exchange for Fernando Tatis Jr. and Erik Johnson.

3. On July 31, 1995, the San Diego Padres traded Andy Benes and a player to be named later (Greg Keagle) to the Seattle Mariners in exchange for Ron Villone and Marc Newfield.

4. On December 15, 1980, the San Diego Padres traded Randy Jones to the New York Mets in exchange for Jose Moreno and John Pacella.

5. On July 22, 2014, the San Diego Padres traded Chase Headley and cash considerations to the New York Yankees in exchange for Yangervis Solarte and Jose Rafael de Paula. Headley then was traded back to the Padres by the Yankees in 2017.

6. On July 30, 2005, the San Diego Padres traded Phil Nevin to the Texas Rangers in exchange for Chan Ho Park and cash considerations.

7. On August 26, 2003, the San Diego Padres traded Jason Bay, Óliver Pérez, and a player to be named later (Cory

Stewart) to the Pittsburgh Pirates in exchange for Brian Giles.

8. On November 18, 1974, the San Diego Padres traded Nate Colbert to the Detroit Tigers in exchange for Dick Sharon, Bob Strampe, and Ed Brinkman.

9. On December 8, 1980, the San Diego Padres traded Rollie Fingers, Gene Tenace, Bob Shirley, and a player to be named later (Bob Geren) to the St. Louis Cardinals in exchange for Terry Kennedy, John Littlefield, Al Olmsted, Mike Phillips, Kim Seamen, Steve Swisher, and John Urrea.

10. On December 22, 1999, the San Diego Padres traded Wally Joyner, Reggie Sanders, and Quilvio Veras to the Atlanta Braves in exchange for Ryan Klesko, Bret Boone, and Jason Shiell.

CHAPTER 8:

DRAFT DAY

QUIZ TIME!

1. Dave Winfield was drafted by the San Diego Padres with which pick in the first round of the 1973 MLB draft?

   a. 1st

   b. 2nd

   c. 3rd

   d. 4th

2. Trevor Hoffman was drafted by which team in the 11th round of the 1989 MLB draft?

   a. San Diego Padres

   b. Milwaukee Brewers

   c. Cincinnati Reds

   d. Florida Marlins

3. Jake Peavy was drafted by the San Diego Padres in which round of the 1999 MLB draft?

   a. 13th

   b. 15th

c. 17th

d. 20th

4. Adrian Gonzalez was drafted by which team with the first overall pick of the 2000 MLB draft?

a. Florida Marlins

b. Los Angeles Dodgers

c. Texas Rangers

d. Boston Red Sox

5. Randy Jones was drafted by the San Diego Padres in which round of the 1972 MLB draft?

a. 2nd

b. 3rd

c. 4th

d. 5th

6. With which pick in the first round of the 1988 MLB draft did the Padres select Andy Benes?

a. 1st

b. 2nd

c. 10th

d. 12th

7. Tony Gwynn was drafted by the San Diego Padres in the third round of the 1981 MLB draft out of San Diego State University.

a. True

b. False

8. Gene Tenace was drafted by which team in the 20th round of the 1965 MLB draft?

   a. St. Louis Cardinals
   b. Los Angeles Dodgers
   c. Kansas City Athletics
   d. Pittsburgh Pirates

9. With which pick in the first round of the 1975 MLB draft did the Padres selected Gene Richards?

   a. 1st
   b. 5th
   c. 9th
   d. 11th

10. Chase Headley was drafted by the San Diego Padres in the second round of the 2005 MLB draft.

    a. True
    b. False

11. With the first overall pick of the 1992 MLB draft, which team selected Phil Nevin?

    a. San Diego Padres
    b. Houston Astros
    c. Detroit Tigers
    d. Texas Rangers

12. Ken Caminiti was drafted by the Houston Astros in the third round of the 1984 MLB draft.

    a. True
    b. False

13. Brian Giles was drafted by which team in the 17th round of the 1989 MLB draft?

    a. San Diego Padres
    b. Pittsburgh Pirates
    c. Cleveland Indians
    d. Atlanta Braves

14. With the third overall pick of the 2010 MLB draft, which team selected Manny Machado?

    a. Los Angeles Dodgers
    b. Baltimore Orioles
    c. Chicago Cubs
    d. San Diego Padres

15. With the third overall pick of the 2008 MLB draft, which team selected Eric Hosmer?

    a. San Diego Padres
    b. Seattle Mariners
    c. Chicago White Sox
    d. Kansas City Royals

16. Eric Show was drafted by the San Diego Padres in which round of the 1978 MLB draft?

    a. 10th
    b. 15th
    c. 18th
    d. 20th

17. Wil Myers was drafted by which team in the third round of the 2009 MLB draft?

a. Kansas City Royals

b. Tampa Bay Rays

c. Philadelphia Phillies

d. Washington Nationals

18. Terry Kennedy was drafted by which team in the first round with the sixth overall selection of the 1977 MLB draft?

a. San Francisco Giants

b. St. Louis Cardinals

c. Baltimore Orioles

d. New York Mets

19. Ed Whitson was drafted by which team in the sixth round of the 1974 MLB draft?

a. New York Yankees

b. Cleveland Indians

c. San Francisco Giants

d. Pittsburgh Pirates

20. Tony Gwynn Jr. was drafted by the Milwaukee Brewers in the second round of the 2003 MLB draft out of San Diego State University.

a. True

b. False

QUIZ ANSWERS

1. D – 4th

2. C – Cincinnati Reds

3. B – 15th

4. A – Florida Marlins

5. D – 5th

6. A – 1st

7. A – True

8. C – Kansas City Athletics

9. A – 1st

10. A – True

11. B – Houston Astros

12. A – True

13. C – Cleveland Indians

14. B – Baltimore Orioles

15. D – Kansas City Royals

16. C – 18th

17. A – Kansas City Royals

18. B – St. Louis Cardinals

19. D – Pittsburgh Pirates

20. A – True

DID YOU KNOW?

1. Ryan Klesko was drafted in the fifth round of the 1989 MLB draft by the Atlanta Braves.

2. Greg Harris was drafted in the 10th round of the 1985 MLB draft by the San Diego Padres.

3. Joey Hamilton was drafted eighth overall in the first round of the 1991 MLB draft by the San Diego Padres.

4. Bruce Hurst was drafted 22nd overall in the first round of the 1976 MLB draft by the Boston Red Sox.

5. Will Venable was drafted in the seventh round of the 2005 MLB draft by the San Diego Padres.

6. Austin Hedges was drafted in the second round of the 2011 MLB draft by the San Diego Padres.

7. Wally Joyner was drafted in the third round of the 1983 MLB draft by the California Angels.

8. Rickey Henderson was drafted in the fourth round of the 1976 MLB draft by the Oakland Athletics.

9. Steve Finley was drafted in the 13th round of the 1987 MLB draft by the Baltimore Orioles.

10. Ozzie Smith was drafted in the fourth round of the 1977 MLB draft by the San Diego Padres.

CHAPTER 9:

ODDS & ENDS

QUIZ TIME!

1. While in college, former Padres outfielder Dave Winfield was arrested for stealing what item?

    a. Snowblower

    b. Bag of chips

    c. Baseball glove

    d. Lawnmower

2. Former Padres manager Bud Black earned a bachelor's degree in management from San Diego State University.

    a. True

    b. False

3. Which former Padres player coached the American League team in the 2010 Taco Bell All-Star Legends & Celebrity Softball Game?

    a. Tony Gwynn

    b. Rickey Henderson

    c. Goose Gossage

    d. Steve Garvey

4. Former Padres first baseman Yonder Alonso is the brother-in-law of which current Padres player?

   a. Wil Myers
   b. Manny Machado
   c. Fernando Tatis Jr.
   d. Eric Hosmer

5. Ozzie Smith's son was a top 10 finalist on which TV show?

   a. *America's Got Talent*
   b. *Survivor*
   c. *Big Brother*
   d. *American Idol*

6. In 2008, Joe Carter appeared on an episode of what reality show?

   a. *Wipeout*
   b. *The Real Housewives of Orange County*
   c. *Pros vs. Joes*
   d. *Diners, Drive-Ins and Dives*

7. Former Padres manager Bruce Bochy wrote a book in 2015, *A Book of Walks,* that highlights his love of walking around cities he visited as an MLB manager.

   a. True
   b. False

8. When Cito Gaston played for the Atlanta Braves, he was a roommate of Hank Aaron.

a. True

b. False

9. Former Padres manager Bud Black is the current manager of which MLB team?

   a. Kansas City Royals

   b. Los Angeles Angels

   c. Toronto Blue Jays

   d. Colorado Rockies

10. David Ross was the first MLB contestant on which show?

    a. *Celebrity MasterChef*

    b. *Big Brother*

    c. *Celebrity Drag Race*

    d. *Dancing with the Stars*

11. What reality show did Jim Edmonds star on with his ex-wife Meghan?

    a. *Vanderpump Rules*

    b. *90-Day Fiancé*

    c. *The Real Housewives of Orange County*

    d. *The Amazing Race*

12. Former Padres Justin Upton and B.J. Upton are brothers.

    a. True

    b. False

13. Rollie Fingers is known for what part of his body?

    a. Mullet

    b. Handlebar mustache

c. Mutton chops

d. Two different colored eyes

14. Fernando Tatis Jr.'s father, Fernando Tatis Sr., played in MLB from 1997 to 2010.

    a. True

    b. False

15. Terry Kennedy is currently a scout for which MLB team?

    a. Baltimore Orioles

    b. St. Louis Cardinals

    c. Chicago Cubs

    d. San Francisco Giants

16. Gaylord Perry's brother, Jim Perry, also pitched in MLB.

    a. True

    b. False

17. Will Venable is the current bench coach for which MLB team?

    a. Chicago Cubs

    b. Boston Red Sox

    c. Texas Rangers

    d. Los Angeles Dodgers

18. Phil Nevin is the current third base coach for which MLB team?

    a. Minnesota Twins

    b. Detroit Tigers

    c. Houston Astros

    d. New York Yankees

19. Which MLB legend is the uncle of Gary Sheffield?

    a. Darryl Strawberry
    b. Hank Aaron
    c. Dwight Gooden
    d. Reggie Jackson

20. Manny Machado has a dog named "Kobe" after basketball legend Kobe Bryant.

    a. True
    b. False

QUIZ ANSWERS

1. A – Snowblower

2. A – True

3. C – Goose Gossage

4. B – Manny Machado

5. D – *American Idol*

6. C – *Pros vs. Joes*

7. A – True

8. A – True

9. D – Colorado Rockies

10. D – *Dancing with the Stars*

11. C – *The Real Housewives of Orange County*

12. A – True

13. B – Handlebar mustache

14. A – True

15. C – Chicago Cubs

16. A – True

17. B – Boston Red Sox

18. D – New York Yankees

19. C – Dwight Gooden

20. A – True

DID YOU KNOW?

1. Drew Pomeranz is the great-grandson of professional baseball/professional football player Garland Buckeye.

2. Brad Ausmus was inducted into the National Jewish Sports Hall of Fame in 2004.

3. Rickey Henderson is known for referring to himself in the third person.

4. Padres pitcher Joe Musgrove was born nearby in El Cajon, California.

5. Sixto Lezcano used to be the batting coach for the Danville Braves, the rookie affiliate of the Atlanta Braves.

6. Growing up, Blake Snell was a fan of the Seattle Mariners.

7. Tony Gwynn Jr. is a current broadcaster for Padres TV and radio networks.

8. Graig Nettles is mentioned in the music video for "Glory Days" by Bruce Springsteen.

9. In 2015, Matt Stairs was inducted into the Canadian Baseball Hall of Fame.

10. San Diego Padres players in the California Sports Hall of Fame include Tony Gwynn, Steve Garvey, Dave Winfield, and Fernando Valenzuela.

CHAPTER 10:

OUTFIELDERS

QUIZ TIME!

1. How old was Tony Gwynn when he made his MLB debut with the Padres?

    a. 21

    b. 22

    c. 23

    d. 24

2. Dave Winfield spent eight seasons of his MLB career with the San Diego Padres.

    a. True

    b. False

3. How many Gold Glove Awards did Steve Finley win during his 19-season MLB career?

    a. 1

    b. 3

    c. 5

    d. 7

4. Brian Giles was named to two All-Star Games in his 15-season MLB career.

    a. True
    b. False

5. How many Silver Slugger Awards has Justin Upton won?

    a. 1
    b. 2
    c. 3
    d. 4

6. Gene Richards spent seven seasons of his MLB career with the San Diego Padres and one season with which other franchise?

    a. Texas Rangers
    b. Montreal Expos
    c. San Francisco Giants
    d. Florida Marlins

7. Ryan Klesko was named the 1994 National League Rookie of the Year.

    a. True
    b. False

8. How many seasons did Will Venable spend with the San Diego Padres?

    a. 2
    b. 4
    c. 6
    d. 8

9. Wil Myers was named the American League Rookie of the Year for which season?

   a. 2011
   b. 2012
   c. 2013
   d. 2014

10. How many seasons did Cito Gaston spend with the San Diego Padres?

    a. 3
    b. 4
    c. 5
    d. 6

11. During his 13-season MLB career, Bobby Tolan played for the San Diego Padres, Cincinnati Reds, Philadelphia Phillies, Pittsburgh Pirates, and which other team?

    a. St. Louis Cardinals
    b. Oakland A's
    c. Los Angeles Dodgers
    d. New York Yankees

12. Reggie Sanders was named to one All-Star Game in his 17-season MLB career.

    a. True
    b. False

13. Former Padres outfielder Mark Kotsay is the current third base coach for which MLB team?

a. Miami Marlins

b. Boston Red Sox

c. Oakland A's

d. Chicago White Sox

14. What year was Rickey Henderson inducted into the National Baseball Hall of Fame?

a. 2008

b. 2009

c. 2010

d. 2011

15. How many All-Star Games was Carlos Quentin named to in his nine-season MLB career?

a. 1

b. 2

c. 3

d. 4

16. How many Silver Slugger Awards did Gary Sheffield win in his 22-season MLB career?

a. 3

b. 4

c. 5

d. 6

17. Former Padres outfielder and manager Dave Roberts is the current manager of which MLB team?

a. Cleveland Indians

b. Los Angeles Dodgers

c. Boston Red Sox

d. Washington Nationals

18. How many All-Star Games was Joe Carter named to in his 16-season MLB career?

    a. 2

    b. 3

    c. 4

    d. 5

19. How many Gold Glove Awards did Mike Cameron win in his 17-season MLB career?

    a. 1

    b. 2

    c. 3

    d. 4

20. Trent Grisham won his first career Gold Glove with the Padres in 2020.

    a. True

    b. False

QUIZ ANSWERS

1. B – 22

2. A – True

3. C – 5

4. A – True

5. C – 3

6. C – San Francisco Giants

7. B – False (He finished third.)

8. D – 8

9. C – 2013

10. D – 6

11. A – St. Louis Cardinals

12. A – True

13. C – Oakland A's

14. B – 2009

15. B – 2

16. C – 5

17. B – Los Angeles Dodgers

18. D – 5

19. C – 3

20. A – True

DID YOU KNOW?

1. Tony Gwynn spent his entire 20-season MLB career with the San Diego Padres. He is a member of the National Baseball Hall of Fame, 15-time All-Star, five-time Gold Glove Award winner, seven-time Silver Slugger Award winner, and eight-time NL batting champion.

2. Dave Winfield spent eight seasons of his 22-season MLB career with the San Diego Padres. He also played for the New York Yankees, Minnesota Twins, California Angels, Cleveland Indians, and Toronto Blue Jays. He is a member of the National Baseball Hall of Fame, 12-time All-Star, seven-time Gold Glove Award winner, six-time Silver Slugger Award winner, and a World Series champion.

3. Steve Finley spent four seasons of his 19-season MLB career with the San Diego Padres. He also played for the Arizona Diamondbacks, Houston Astros, Baltimore Orioles, Colorado Rockies, San Francisco Giants, Los Angeles Dodgers, and Los Angeles Angels. He is a two-time All-Star, five-time Gold Glove Award winner, and a World Series champion.

4. Brian Giles spent seven seasons of his 15-season MLB career with the San Diego Padres. He also played for the Pittsburgh Pirates and Cleveland Indians. He is a two-time All-Star.

5. Rickey Henderson spent three seasons of his 25-season MLB career with the San Diego Padres. He also played for the Oakland A's, New York Yankees, New York Mets, Boston Red Sox, Los Angeles Dodgers, Anaheim Angels, Seattle Mariners, and Toronto Blue Jays. He is a member of the National Baseball Hall of Fame, 1990 AL MVP, 10-time All-Star, two-time World Series champion, 1981 Gold Glove Award winner, three-time Silver Slugger Award winner, and 1989 ALCS MVP.

6. Gary Sheffield spent two seasons of his 22-season MLB career with the San Diego Padres. He also played for the New York Yankees, Florida Marlins, Los Angeles Dodgers, Milwaukee Brewers, Atlanta Braves, Detroit Tigers, and New York Mets. He is a nine-time All-Star, five-time Silver Slugger Award winner, 1992 NL batting champion, 1992 Major League Player of the Year, and a World Series champion.

7. Ryan Klesko spent seven seasons of his 16-season MLB career with the San Diego Padres. He also played for the Atlanta Braves and San Francisco Giants. He was named an All-Star in 2001 and is a World Series champion.

8. Joe Carter spent one year of his 16-season MLB career with the San Diego Padres. He also played for the Toronto Blue Jays, Cleveland Indians, Chicago Cubs, San Francisco Giants, and Baltimore Orioles. He is a five-time All-Star, two-time Silver Slugger Award winner, and two-time World Series champion.

9. Cito Gaston spent six seasons of his 11-season MLB career with the San Diego Padres. He also played for the Atlanta Braves and Pittsburgh Pirates. He was an All-Star in 1970.

10. Wil Myers has been with the San Diego Padres since 2015. He has also played for the Tampa Bay Rays. He was named an All-Star in 2016 and was the 2013 American League Rookie of the Year.

CHAPTER 11:

INFIELDERS

QUIZ TIME!

1. How many All-Star Games was Adrian Gonzalez named to in his 15-season MLB career?

   a. 1

   b. 3

   c. 5

   d. 7

2. Phil Nevin spent seven seasons of his MLB career with the San Diego Padres.

   a. True

   b. False

3. Chase Headley spent nine seasons of his MLB career with the San Diego Padres and the other four seasons with which franchise?

   a. Seattle Mariners

   b. Colorado Rockies

   c. Oakland A's

   d. New York Yankees

4. How many Gold Glove Awards did Ken Caminiti win in his 15-season MLB career?

   a. 1
   b. 2
   c. 3
   d. 4

5. How many All-Star Games was Nate Colbert named to in his 10-season MLB career?

   a. 1
   b. 2
   c. 3
   d. 4

6. Eric Hosmer has played for the San Diego Padres and which other team?

   a. Miami Marlins
   b. Kansas City Royals
   c. Tampa Bay Rays
   d. Oakland A's

7. Fernando Tatis Jr. was named the 2019 NL Rookie of the Year.

   a. True
   b. False

8. How many All-Star Games has Manny Machado been named to?

   a. 2
   b. 3

c. 4

d. 5

9. How many Silver Slugger Awards did Fred McGriff win during his 19-season MLB career?

   a. 1

   b. 2

   c. 3

   d. 4

10. How many Gold Glove Awards did Tony Fernández win in his 17-season MLB career?

   a. 1

   b. 2

   c. 3

   d. 4

11. What year was Ozzie Smith inducted into the National Baseball Hall of Fame?

   a. 2000

   b. 2002

   c. 2003

   d. 2004

12. Bret Boone won four Gold Glove Awards in his 14-season MLB career.

   a. True

   b. False

13. During his 16-season MLB career, Wally Joyner played for the San Diego Padres, Kansas City Royals, Atlanta Braves, and which other franchise?

    a. St. Louis Cardinals
    b. Los Angeles Dodgers
    c. California/Anaheim Angels
    d. Houston Astros

14. During his 22-season MLB career, Willie McCovey played for the San Diego Padres, Oakland A's, and which team?

    a. Boston Red Sox
    b. New York Yankees
    c. Los Angeles Dodgers
    d. San Francisco Giants

15. How many All-Star Games was David Eckstein named to in his 10-season MLB career?

    a. 0
    b. 1
    c. 2
    d. 3

16. Tim Flannery spent his entire 11-season MLB career with the San Diego Padres.

    a. True
    b. False

17. What year was Roberto Alomar inducted into the National Baseball Hall of Fame?

a. 2010

b. 2011

c. 2012

d. 2013

18. How many seasons did Garry Templeton spend with the San Diego Padres?

  a. 6

  b. 8

  c. 10

  d. 12

19. How many seasons did Bip Roberts spend with the San Diego Padres?

  a. 1

  b. 3

  c. 5

  d. 7

20. Steve Garvey spent five seasons with the San Diego Padres and the other 14 seasons of his MLB career with the Los Angeles Dodgers.

  a. True

  b. False

QUIZ ANSWERS

1. C – 5

2. A – True

3. D – New York Yankees

4. C – 3

5. C – 3

6. B – Kansas City Royals

7. B – False (He finished third.)

8. C – 4

9. C – 3

10. D – 4

11. B – 2002

12. A – True

13. C – California/Anaheim Angels

14. D – San Francisco Giants

15. C – 2

16. A – True

17. B – 2011

18. C – 10

19. D – 7

20. A – True

DID YOU KNOW?

1. Adrian Gonzalez spent five seasons of his 15-season MLB career with the San Diego Padres. He also played for the Boston Red Sox, Los Angeles Dodgers, Texas Rangers, and New York Mets. He is a five-time All-Star, four-time Gold Glove Award winner, and two-time Silver Slugger Award winner.

2. Ken Caminiti spent four seasons of his 15-season MLB career with the San Diego Padres. He also played for the Houston Astros, Texas Rangers, and Atlanta Braves. He was a three-time All-Star, 1996 NL MVP, three-time Gold Glove Award winner, and 1996 Silver Slugger Award winner.

3. Chase Headley spent nine seasons of his 12-season MLB career with the San Diego Padres. He also played for the New York Yankees. He is a 2012 Gold Glove Award winner and 2012 Silver Slugger Award winner.

4. Nate Colbert spent six seasons of his 10-season MLB career with the San Diego Padres. He also played for the Montreal Expos, Houston Astros, Detroit Tigers, and Oakland A's. He is a three-time All-Star.

5. Fernando Tatis Jr. has played for the San Diego Padres since his MLB debut in 2019. He won a Silver Slugger Award in 2020 after finishing third in the Rookie of the Year race in 2019.

6. Eric Hosmer has been with the San Diego Padres since 2018. He previously played for the Kansas City Royals from 2011 to 2017. He was an All-Star in 2016, is a four-time Gold Glove Award winner, a 2017 Silver Slugger Award winner, 2016 All-Star Game MVP, and a World Series champion.

7. Manny Machado has been with the San Diego Padres since 2019. He also spent seven seasons with the Baltimore Orioles and 66 games with the Los Angeles Dodgers. So far in his career, he is a four-time All-Star, two-time Gold Glove Award winner, 2013 Platinum Glove Award winner, and 2020 Silver Slugger Award winner.

8. Roberto Alomar spent three of his 17 MLB seasons with the San Diego Padres. He also played for the Toronto Blue Jays, Cleveland Indians, Baltimore Orioles, New York Mets, Chicago White Sox, and Arizona Diamondbacks. He is a member of the National Baseball Hall of Fame, 12-time All-Star, two-time World Series champion, 10-time Gold Glove Award winner, four-time Silver Slugger Award winner, 1992 ALCS MVP, and 1998 All-Star Game MVP.

9. Ozzie Smith spent four seasons of his 19-season MLB career with the San Diego Padres. He also played for the St. Louis Cardinals. He is a member of the National Baseball Hall of Fame, 15-time All-Star, 13-time Gold Glove Award winner, 1987 Silver Slugger Award winner, 1985 NLCS MVP, and a World Series champion.

10. Steve Garvey spent five seasons of his 19-season MLB career with the San Diego Padres. He also played for the Los Angeles Dodgers. He is a 10-time All-Star, four-time Gold Glove Award winner, 1974 NL MVP, two-time NLCS MVP, two-time All-Star Game MVP, and a World Series champion.

CHAPTER 12:

PITCHERS AND CATCHERS

QUIZ TIME!

1. What year was Trevor Hoffman inducted into the National Baseball Hall of Fame?

    a. 2016
    b. 2017
    c. 2018
    d. 2019

2. Jake Peavy spent eight seasons of his MLB career with the San Diego Padres.

    a. True
    b. False

3. How many All-Star Games was Andy Ashby named to in his 14-season MLB career?

    a. 1
    b. 2
    c. 3
    d. 4

4. Randy Jones spent eight seasons of his MLB career with the San Diego Padres and the other two seasons with which team?

    a. New York Yankees
    b. California Angels
    c. Los Angeles Dodgers
    d. New York Mets

5. How many All-Star Games was Andy Benes named to in his 14-season MLB career?

    a. 0
    b. 1
    c. 2
    d. 3

6. During his 15-season MLB career, Gene Tenace played for the San Diego Padres, St. Louis Cardinals, Pittsburgh Pirates, and which other team?

    a. Kansas City Royals
    b. Cleveland Indians
    c. Oakland A's
    d. Philadelphia Phillies

7. Benito Santiago was named the 1987 National League Rookie of the Year.

    a. True
    b. False

8. How many All-Star Games was Terry Kennedy named to in his 14-season MLB career?

a. 1

b. 2

c. 3

d. 4

9. In his 11-season MLB career, Eric Show spent 10 seasons with the San Diego Padres and one season with which franchise?

a. Oakland A's

b. Minnesota Twins

c. Los Angeles Dodgers

d. Chicago Cubs

10. How many seasons did Ed Whitson spend with the San Diego Padres?

a. 2

b. 4

c. 6

d. 8

11. What year was Goose Gossage inducted into the National Baseball Hall of Fame?

a. 2006

b. 2007

c. 2008

d. 2009

12. Gaylord Perry was inducted into the National Baseball Hall of Fame in 1991.

a. True

b. False

13. How many All-Star Games was Mike Piazza named to in his 16-season MLB career?

    a. 3
    b. 8
    c. 10
    d. 12

14. During his 18-season MLB career, Brad Ausmus played for the San Diego Padres, Detroit Tigers, Los Angeles Dodgers, and which franchise?

    a. New York Yankees
    b. Houston Astros
    c. Florida Marlins
    d. Arizona Diamondbacks

15. How many All-Star Games was Heath Bell named to in his 11-season MLB career?

    a. 1
    b. 2
    c. 3
    d. 4

16. Huston Street was named the 2005 American League Rookie of the Year.

    a. True
    b. False

17. What year was Rollie Fingers inducted into the National Baseball Hall of Fame?

a. 1990

b. 1991

c. 1992

d. 1993

18. How many seasons did Greg Harris spend with the San Diego Padres?

    a. 2

    b. 4

    c. 6

    d. 8

19. How many All-Star Games was Bruce Hurst named to in his 15-season MLB career?

    a. 0

    b. 1

    c. 2

    d. 3

20. In his 13-season MLB career, Sterling Hitchcock played for the San Diego Padres, New York Yankees, St. Louis Cardinals, and Seattle Mariners.

    a. True

    b. False

QUIZ ANSWERS

1. C – 2018

2. A – True

3. B – 2

4. D – New York Mets

5. B – 1

6. C – Oakland A's

7. A – True

8. D – 4

9. A – Oakland A's

10. D – 8

11. C – 2008

12. A – True

13. D – 12

14. B – Houston Astros

15. C – 3

16. A – True

17. C – 1992

18. C – 6

19. B – 1

20. A – True

DID YOU KNOW?

1. Trevor Hoffman spent 16 seasons of his 18-season MLB career with the San Diego Padres. He also played for the Milwaukee Brewers and Florida Marlins. He is a member of the National Baseball Hall of Fame, seven-time All-Star, and two-time Rolaids Relief Man of the Year Award winner.

2. Jake Peavy spent eight seasons of his 15-season MLB career with the San Diego Padres. He also played for the San Francisco Giants, Boston Red Sox, and Chicago White Sox. He is a three-time All-Star, 2012 Gold Glove Award winner, 2007 pitching Triple Crown winner, two-time leader in ERA, two-time World Series champion, and 2007 NL Cy Young Award winner.

3. Randy Jones spent eight seasons of his 10-season MLB career with the San Diego Padres. He also played for the New York Mets. He is a two-time All-Star, 1976 NL Cy Young Award winner, and led the NL in ERA in 1975.

4. Gene Tenace spent four seasons of his 15-season MLB career with the San Diego Padres. He also played for the Oakland A's, St. Louis Cardinals, and Pittsburgh Pirates. He is a 1975 All-Star, four-time World Series champion, and 1972 World Series MVP.

5. Benito Santiago spent seven seasons of his 20-season MLB career with the San Diego Padres. He also played for the

San Francisco Giants, Cincinnati Reds, Florida Marlins, Toronto Blue Jays, Kansas City Royals, Pittsburgh Pirates, Philadelphia Phillies, and Chicago Cubs. He is the 1987 NL Rookie of the Year Award winner, a five-time All-Star, three-time Gold Glove Award winner, four-time Silver Slugger Award winner, and 2002 NLCS MVP.

6. Terry Kennedy spent six seasons of his 14-season MLB career with the San Diego Padres. He also played for the San Francisco Giants, St. Louis Cardinals, and Baltimore Orioles. He is a four-time All-Star and 1983 Silver Slugger Award.

7. Goose Gossage spent four seasons of his 22-season MLB career with the San Diego Padres. He also played for the New York Yankees, Oakland A's, Chicago White Sox, Pittsburgh Pirates, San Francisco Giants, Texas Rangers, Chicago Cubs, and Seattle Mariners. He is a member of the National Baseball Hall of Fame, nine-time All-Star, 1978 Rolaids Relief Man of the Year Award winner, and a World Series champion.

8. Rollie Fingers spent four seasons of his 17-season MLB career with the San Diego Padres. He also played for the Oakland A's and Milwaukee Brewers. He is a member of the National Baseball Hall of Fame, seven-time All-Star, 1981 AL MVP, 1981 AL Cy Young Award winner, four-time Rolaids Relief Man of the Year Award winner, three-time World Series champion, and 1974 World Series MVP.

9. Brad Ausmus spent four seasons of his 18-season MLB career with the San Diego Padres. He also played for the Houston Astros, Detroit Tigers, and Los Angeles Dodgers. He is a three-time Gold Glove Award winner and 1999 All-Star.

10. Gaylord Perry spent two seasons of his 22-season MLB career with the San Diego Padres. He also played for the San Francisco Giants, Texas Rangers, Cleveland Indians, Seattle Mariners, Kansas City Royals, Atlanta Braves, and New York Yankees. He is a member of the National Baseball Hall of Fame, five-time All-Star, and two-time Cy Young Award winner.

CHAPTER 13:

WORLD SERIES

QUIZ TIME!

1. How many World Series championships have the San Diego Padres won?

    a. 0

    b. 1

    c. 2

    d. 3

2. How many NL pennants have the San Diego Padres won?

    a. 0

    b. 1

    c. 2

    d. 3

3. How many wild card berths have the San Diego Padres won?

    a. 0

    b. 1

    c. 2

    d. 3

4. Which team did the San Diego Padres face in the 1984 World Series?

    a. Kansas City Royals
    b. Detroit Tigers
    c. Toronto Blue Jays
    d. California Angels

5. What team did the San Diego Padres face in the 1998 World Series?

    a. Texas Rangers
    b. Cleveland Indians
    c. Boston Red Sox
    d. New York Yankees

6. Who was the manager of the San Diego Padres during the 1984 World Series?

    a. Bruce Bochy
    b. Larry Bowa
    c. Dick Williams
    d. Roger Craig

7. The 1984 World Series went five games.

    a. True
    b. False

8. Who was the manager of the San Diego Padres during the 1998 World Series?

    a. Bud Black
    b. Bruce Bochy

c. Greg Riddoch

d. Dick Williams

9. How many games did the 1998 World Series go?

   a. 4

   b. 5

   c. 6

   d. 7

10. What was the final score of Game 1 of the 1984 World Series?

   a. Padres 3, Tigers 2

   b. Tigers 3, Padres 2

   c. Padres 5, Tigers 3

   d. Tigers 5, Padres 3

11. What was the final score of Game 1 of the 1998 World Series?

   a. Padres 12, Yankees 6

   b. Yankees 12, Padres 6

   c. Padres 9, Yankees 6

   d. Yankees 9, Padres 6

12. The 1984 World Series was the last World Series in which the designated hitter was used for games played in the National League team's ballpark.

   a. True

   b. False

13. Which Padres pitcher was the starting pitcher of Game 1 of the 1984 World Series?

a. Ed Whitson

b. Eric Show

c. Mark Thurmond

d. Tim Lollar

14. Which Padres pitcher was the starting pitcher of Game 1 of the 1998 World Series?

a. Kevin Brown

b. Andy Ashby

c. Joey Hamilton

d. Sterling Hitchcock

15. What was the final score of Game 5 of the 1984 World Series?

a. Tigers 10, Padres 5

b. Padres 10, Tigers 5

c. Tigers 8, Padres 4

d. Padres 8, Tigers 4

16. 1998 was the first time the same city hosted both the World Series and the Super Bowl in the same year. Not only were they both held in San Diego, but they were also held at the same stadium, Qualcomm Stadium.

a. True

b. False

17. What was the final score of Game 4 of the 1998 World Series?

a. Yankees 4, Padres 2

b. Yankees 3, Padres 1

c. Yankees 4, Padres 0

d. Yankees 3, Padres 0

18. Which two players were the only two Padres to hit at least one home run in the 1984 World Series?

a. Bruce Bochy and Tim Flannery

b. Terry Kennedy and Kurt Bevacqua

c. Tony Gwynn and Steve Garvey

d. Tony Gwynn and Terry Kennedy

19. Which two players were the only two Padres to hit at least one home run in the 1998 World Series?

a. Tony Gwynn and Wally Joyner

b. Ken Caminiti and Steve Finley

c. Tony Gwynn and Greg Vaughn

d. Greg Vaughn and Ruben Rivera

20. Steve Garvey was named the 1984 NLCS MVP and Sterling Hitchcock was named the 1998 NLCS MVP.

a. True

b. False

QUIZ ANSWERS

1. A – 0

2. C – 2

3. B – 1

4. B – Detroit Tigers

5. D – New York Yankees

6. C – Dick Williams

7. A – True

8. B – Bruce Bochy

9. A – 4

10. B – Tigers 3, Padres 2

11. D – Yankees 9, Padres 6

12. A - True

13. C – Mark Thurmond

14. A – Kevin Brown

15. C – Tigers 8, Padres 4

16. A – True

17. D – Yankees 3, Padres 0

18. B – Terry Kennedy and Kurt Bevacqua

19. C – Tony Gwynn and Greg Vaughn

20. A – True

DID YOU KNOW?

1. The 1984 World Series took place from October 9 to October 14.

2. The 1998 World Series took place from October 17 to October 21.

3. The 1984 World Series was the first World Series presided over by Commissioner Peter Ueberroth. The 1998 World Series was the first World Series presided over by Commissioner Bud Selig.

4. Andy Hawkins has the only World Series win so far in San Diego Padres history.

5. The San Diego Padres faced the Chicago Cubs in the 1984 NLCS and they faced the Atlanta Braves in the 1998 NLCS.

6. The 1984 World Series was broadcast on NBC with announcers Vin Scully and Joe Garagiola. The 1998 World Series was broadcast on Fox with announcers Joe Buck, Tim McCarver, and Bob Brenly.

7. The attendance at Jack Murphy Stadium for Game 1 of the 1984 World Series was 57,908.

8. The attendance at Yankee Stadium for Game 1 of the 1998 World Series was 56,712.

9. Hall-of-Famers who were involved in the 1984 World Series were Dick Williams, Tony Gwynn, Goose Gossage,

Sparky Anderson, Jack Morris, Alan Trammel, and Doug Harvey.

10. Hall-of-Famers who were involved in the 1998 World Series were Tony Gwynn, Trevor Hoffman, Derek Jeter, Mariano Rivera, and Joe Torre.

CHAPTER 14:

HEATED RIVALRIES

QUIZ TIME!

1. Which team does NOT play in the National League West with the San Diego Padres?

   a. Los Angeles Dodgers

   b. Colorado Rockies

   c. Houston Astros

   d. Arizona Diamondbacks

2. The Atlanta Braves were in the National League West from 1969 through 1993.

   a. True

   b. False

3. Which team below was a member of the NL West Division from 1969 through 1993?

   a. Florida Marlins

   b. Milwaukee Brewers

   c. Cincinnati Reds

   d. Chicago Cubs

4. What current National League West team has the most NL West championships?

    a. San Francisco Giants

    b. Los Angeles Dodgers

    c. San Diego Padres

    d. Arizona Diamondbacks

5. The Houston Astros were members of the National League West from 1969 through 1993.

    a. True

    b. False

6. Which team won the National League West in 2020?

    a. Colorado Rockies

    b. Arizona Diamondbacks

    c. San Diego Padres

    d. Los Angeles Dodgers

7. The Colorado Rockies have never won an NL West Division championship.

    a. True

    b. False

8. The Padres have not won a World Series championship. How many have the Los Angeles Dodgers won?

    a. 5

    b. 7

    c. 9

    d. 12

9. The Padres have not won a World Series championship. How many have the Arizona Diamondbacks won?

    a. 0
    b. 1
    c. 2
    d. 3

10. The Padres have not won a World Series championship. How many have the San Francisco Giants won?

    a. 2
    b. 4
    c. 6
    d. 8

11. The Padres have not won a World Series championship. How many have the Colorado Rockies won?

    a. 0
    b. 1
    c. 2
    d. 3

12. The San Diego Padres were members of the American League West division from 1969-1998.

    a. True
    b. False

13. Which player has NOT played for both the San Diego Padres and the Colorado Rockies?

    a. Steve Finley
    b. Jake Peavy

c. Drew Pomeranz

d. Eric Young Sr.

14. Which player has NOT played for both the San Diego Padres and the San Francisco Giants?

    a. Goose Gossage

    b. Gaylord Perry

    c. Bip Roberts

    d. Dave Roberts

15. Which player has NOT played for both the San Diego Padres and the Arizona Diamondbacks?

    a. Roberto Alomar

    b. Justin Upton

    c. Trevor Cahill

    d. Manny Machado

16. The National League West Division was formed in 1969.

    a. True

    b. False

17. Which player has NOT played for both the San Diego Padres and the Los Angeles Dodgers?

    a. Adrian Gonzalez

    b. Goose Gossage

    c. Matt Kemp

    d. Fernando Valenzuela

18. How many National League West Division titles did the Cincinnati Reds win before they moved to the NL Central Division?

a. 0

b. 2

c. 5

d. 7

19. How many National League West Division titles did the Atlanta Braves win before they moved to the NL East Division?

a. 0

b. 1

c. 3

d. 5

20. The Houston Astros won two National League West Division championships before they moved to the NL Central.

a. True

b. False

QUIZ ANSWERS

1. C – Houston Astros

2. A – True

3. C – Cincinnati Reds

4. B – Los Angeles Dodgers (19)

5. A – True

6. D – Los Angeles Dodgers

7. A – True

8. B – 7

9. B – 1

10. D – 8

11. A – 0

12. B – False

13. B – Jake Peavy

14. C – Bip Roberts

15. D – Manny Machado

16. A – True

17. B – Goose Gossage

18. D – 7

19. D – 5

20. A – True

DID YOU KNOW?

1. The Los Angeles Dodgers have won the most National League West championships with 19. The San Francisco Giants have won eight, the San Diego Padres and Arizona Diamondbacks have won five each and the Colorado Rockies have yet to win one. The Cincinnati Reds won seven division championships during their time in the NL West, the Atlanta Braves won five division championships during their time in the NL West, and the Houston Astros won two division championships during their time in the NL West. The most recent NL West Division champion was the Los Angeles Dodgers on their way to winning the 2020 World Series.

2. The Atlanta Braves were the first National League West Division champions in 1969.

3. The Los Angeles Dodgers, San Diego Padres, and San Francisco Giants are all founding members of the National League West. The Rockies joined as an expansion team in 1993 and the Arizona Diamondbacks joined as an expansion team in 1998.

4. The Los Angeles Dodgers have won two wild card berths, the San Francisco Giants have earned three, and the Arizona Diamondbacks and San Diego Padres each have one. However, the Colorado Rockies have the most wild card berths in the NL West with five.

5. The Colorado Rockies and San Diego Padres are the only teams in the National League West who have not yet won a World Series championship.

6. The last time the San Diego Padres won the NL West was in 2006.

7. Sandy Alomar, Yonder Alonso, Andy Ashby, Clint Barmes, Jhoulys Chacin, Jeff Cirillo, Jack Cust, Adam Eaton, Alan Embree, Steve Finley, Greg Harris, Ramon Hernandez, Nick Hundley, Bruce Hurst, Matt Kemp, Kevin Kouzmanoff, Drew Pomeranz, Seth Smith, Huston Street, John Vander Wal, Greg Vaughn, Jay Witasick, and Eric Young Sr. have all played for both the San Diego Padres and the Colorado Rockies.

8. Mike Aldrete, Matty Alou, Trevor Cahill, Mike Caldwell, Joe Carter, Alan Embree, Steve Finley, Jeff Francoeur, Tito Fuentes, Goose Gossage, Nick Hundley, Terry Kennedy, Ryan Klesko, Willie McCovey, Mark Melancon, Kevin Mitchell, Xavier Nady, Jake Peavy, Gaylord Perry, Drew Pomeranz, Gene Richards, Dave Roberts, Hector Sanchez, Reggie Sanders, Benito Santiago, Miguel Tejada, John Vander Wal, Ed Whitson, Jay Witasick, and Eric Young Sr. have all played for both the San Diego Padres and the San Francisco Giants.

9. Roberto Alomar, Andy Benes, Heath Bell, Henry Blanco, Craig Breslow, Trevor Cahill, Jhoulys Chacin, Jeff Cirillo, Tony Clark, Jack Cust, David Eckstein, Alan Embree, Steve Finley, Scott Hairston, Orlando Hudson, Edwin

Jackson, Jon Jay, Ian Kennedy, Xavier Nady, Micah Owings, Carlos Quentin, Adam Rosales, Reggie Sanders, and Justin Upton have all played for both the San Diego Padres and the Arizona Diamondbacks.

10. Sandy Alomar, Andy Ashby, Brad Ausmus, Yu Darvish, A.J. Ellis, Steve Finley, Logan Forsythe, Steve Garvey, Adrian Gonzalez, Yasmani Grandal, Tony Gwynn Jr., Jedd Gyorko, Jerry Hairston, Rickey Henderson, Edwin Jackson, Matt Kemp, Mat Latos, Mark Loretta, Manny Machado, Greg Maddux, Mike Piazza, Dave Roberts, David Ross, Gary Sheffield, Bobby Valentine, Fernando Valenzuela, Will Venable, Shane Victorino, and Eric Young Sr. have all played for both the San Diego Padres and the Los Angeles Dodgers.

CHAPTER 15:

THE AWARDS SECTION

QUIZ TIME!

1. Who is the only San Diego Padres player to win a National League MVP Award so far in franchise history?

   a. Tony Gwynn

   b. Ken Caminiti

   c. Trevor Hoffman

   d. Dave Winfield

2. Chase Headley won a Wilson Defensive Player of the Year Award in 2012.

   a. True

   b. False

3. Which San Diego Padres player won the 1997 ESPN ESPY Award for Best Major League Baseball Player?

   a. Steve Finley

   b. Rickey Henderson

   c. Tony Gwynn

   d. Ken Caminiti

4. Which San Diego Padres player was named the 1976 National League Rookie of the Year?

    a. Tito Fuentes
    b. Randy Jones
    c. Butch Metzger
    d. None of the above

5. Which San Diego Padres player won a Silver Slugger Award in 2020?

    a. Manny Machado
    b. Fernando Tatis Jr.
    c. Wil Myers
    d. Both A and B

6. Which San Diego Padres pitcher won an NL Cy Young Award in 1978?

    a. Randy Jones
    b. Gaylord Perry
    c. Rollie Fingers
    d. Eric Rasmussen

7. No San Diego Padres player has ever won the MLB Home Run Derby.

    a. True
    b. False

8. Which San Diego Padres player was named the DHL Hometown Hero (voted by MLB fans as the most outstanding player in franchise history)?

a. Trevor Hoffman

b. Dave Winfield

c. Tony Gwynn

d. Jake Peavy

9. Who was the first San Diego Padres player to win a Gold Glove Award?

a. Dave Winfield

b. Ozzie Smith

c. Tony Gwynn

d. Benito Santiago

10. Who was the first San Diego Padres player to win a Silver Slugger Award?

a. Benito Santiago

b. Garry Templeton

c. Tony Gwynn

d. Terry Kennedy

11. Which San Diego Padres player was named the 1987 National League Rookie of the Year?

a. John Kruk

b. Benito Santiago

c. Steve Garvey

d. Kevin Mitchell

12. Jake Peavy won a Cy Young Award in 2007.

a. True

b. False

13. Which San Diego Padres player won a Gold Glove Award in 2007?

    a. Brian Giles
    b. Adrian Gonzalez
    c. Greg Maddux
    d. Jake Peavy

14. How many NL Rolaids Relief Man of the Year Awards did Rollie Fingers win during his time with the San Diego Padres?

    a. 1
    b. 2
    c. 3
    d. 4

15. Which San Diego Padres pitcher won the 2010 MLB Delivery Man of the Year Award?

    a. Jon Garland
    b. Clayton Richard
    c. Mat Latos
    d. Heath Bell

16. No San Diego Padres manager has ever won the NL Manager of the Year Award.

    a. True
    b. False

17. Which San Diego Padres player won a Silver Slugger Award in 2012?

a. Carlos Quentin
b. Chase Headley
c. Will Venable
d. Both A and B

18. Which San Diego Padres player won a Branch Rickey Award in 1995?

a. Tony Gwynn
b. Steve Finley
c. Brad Ausmus
d. Trevor Hoffman

19. Who was named the 1976 Sporting News NL Pitcher of the Year?

a. Butch Metzger
b. Rick Sawyer
c. Randy Jones
d. Brent Strom

20. Andy Benes was named the 1989 Sporting News NL Rookie Pitcher of the Year.

a. True
b. False

QUIZ ANSWERS

1. B – Ken Caminiti (1996)

2. A – True

3. D – Ken Caminiti

4. C – Butch Metzger

5. D – Both A and B

6. B – Gaylord Perry

7. A – True

8. C – Tony Gwynn

9. A – Dave Winfield (1979)

10. D – Terry Kennedy (1983)

11. B – Benito Santiago

12. A – True

13. C – Greg Maddux

14. C – 3

15. D – Heath Bell

16. B – False (Bruce Bochy- 1996, Bud Black-2010)

17. B – Chase Headley

18. A – Tony Gwynn

19. C – Randy Jones

20. A – True

DID YOU KNOW?

1. The San Diego Padres have had four different players win Cy Young Awards: Randy Jones (1976), Gaylord Perry (1978), Mark Davis (1989), and Jake Peavy (2007).

2. The San Diego Padres have had 12 different players win Silver Slugger Awards: Terry Kennedy (1983), Garry Templeton (1984), Tony Gwynn (1984, 1986, 1987, 1989, 1994, 1995, 1997), Benito Santiago (1987, 1988, 1990, 1991), Fred McGriff (1992), Gary Sheffield (1992), Ken Caminiti (1996), Greg Vaughn (1998), Mark Lorreta (2004), Chase Headley (2012), Fernando Tatis Jr. (2020), and Manny Machado (2020).

3. The San Diego Padres have had two managers named National League Manager of the Year: Bruce Bochy (1996) and Bud Black (2010).

4. The San Diego Padres have had 11 different players win Gold Glove Awards: Dave Winfield (1979, 1980), Ozzie Smith (1980, 1981), Tony Gwynn (1986, 1987, 1989, 1990, 1991), Benito Santiago (1988, 1989, 1990), Steve Finley (1995, 1996), Ken Caminiti (1995, 1996, 1997), Mike Cameron (2006), Greg Maddux (2007), Adrian Gonzalez (2008, 2009), Chase Headley (2012) and Trent Grisham (2020).

5. The San Diego Padres have had one player win a National League MVP Award so far: Ken Caminiti (1996).

121

6. The San Diego Padres have had two different players win the NL Rookie of the Year Award: Butch Metzger (1976) and Benito Santiago (1987).

7. The San Diego Padres have had four different players win the NL Rolaids Relief Man of the Year Award: Rollie Fingers (1977, 1978, 1980), Mark Davis (1989), Trevor Hoffman (1998, 2006), and Heath Bell (2009, 2010).

8. The San Diego Padres have had two different players win the Branch Rickey Award: Tony Gwynn (1995) and Trevor Hoffman (2008).

9. Jerry Coleman won a Ford C. Frick Award in 2005.

10. Gary Sheffield won the 1993 ESPY Award for Best Breakthrough Athlete.

CHAPTER 16:

AMERICA'S FINEST CITY

QUIZ TIME!

1. Which fast food chain was founded in San Diego?

   a. McDonald's

   b. Jack in the Box

   c. Wendy's

   d. Chick-Fil-A

2. The "California Burrito," a burrito stuffed with French fries, originated in San Diego.

   a. True

   b. False

3. Which former president was the first person to drive over the Coronado Bridge?

   a. Bill Clinton

   b. Barack Obama

   c. Ronald Reagan

   d. Jimmy Carter

4. Which classic 1980s film was based on San Diego's Clairemont High School?

    a. *Sixteen Candles*
    b. *Ferris Bueller's Day Off*
    c. *The Breakfast Club*
    d. *Fast Times at Ridgemont High*

5. Which San Diego tourist spot was named the most haunted place in America by the Travel Channel?

    a. Star of India
    b. Hotel del Coronado
    c. The Whaley House
    d. Villa Montezuma

6. San Diego produces more of which food than any other U.S. city?

    a. Watermelons
    b. Onions
    c. Pumpkins
    d. Avocados

7. Comic-Con is held each July in San Diego.

    a. True
    b. False

8. What is the largest wooden structure in the United States?

    a. Mission Basilica San Diego de Alcala
    b. Hotel del Coronado
    c. Cosmopolitan Hotel
    d. U.S. Grant Hotel

9. What is the name of San Diego's former NFL team?

   a. San Diego Dolphins
   b. San Diego Seahawks
   c. San Diego Chargers
   d. San Diego 49ers

10. From the 1930s until the 1970s, San Diego was known as the "_____ Capital of the World."

   a. Chocolate
   b. Cinnamon
   c. Coffee
   d. Tuna

11. Which famous children's author lived and worked in La Jolla, San Diego?

   a. Ronald Dahl
   b. Dr. Seuss
   c. Eric Carle
   d. Beverly Cleary

12. The film *Anchorman: The Legend of Ron Burgundy* is set in San Diego.

   a. True
   b. False

13. Which of the following products was invented in San Diego?

   a. Jell-O
   b. Jolly Ranchers

c. WD-40

d. Dawn Dish Soap

14. The USS Midway is the longest-serving aircraft carrier of the 20th century.

   a. True

   b. False

15. In 2019, the San Diego Trolley ranked in what position for ridership of light rail systems in the United States?

   a. 2nd

   b. 3rd

   c. 4th

   d. 5th

16. The Birch Aquarium in La Jolla is the largest oceanographic museum in the United States.

   a. True

   b. False

17. The San Diego Zoo is the most visited zoo in the United States.

   a. True

   b. False

18. What is San Diego International Airport's code?

   a. SDI

   b. SDO

   c. SAN

   d. SDA

19. Which famous board game was created in San Diego?

    a. Clue
    b. Candy Land
    c. Monopoly
    d. Scrabble

20. Balboa Park is almost twice the size of New York City's Central Park.

    a. True
    b. False

QUIZ ANSWERS

1. B – Jack in the Box

2. A - True

3. C – Ronald Reagan

4. D – *Fast Times at Ridgemont High*

5. C – The Whaley House

6. D – Avocados

7. A – True

8. B – Hotel del Coronado

9. C – San Diego Chargers

10. D – Tuna

11. B – Dr. Seuss

12. A – True ("Stay Classy, San Diego")

13. C – WD-40

14. A – True

15. D – 5th

16. A – True

17. A – True

18. C – SAN

19. B – Candy Land

20. A – True

DID YOU KNOW?

1. Snowboarder, skateboarder, and three-time Olympic Gold medalist Shaun White was born in San Diego.

2. The Giant Dipper wooden roller coaster at Belmont Park was the first roller coaster in America to be on the National Register of Historic Places.

3. All lakes in San Diego are manmade.

4. The top employer in the city of San Diego is the United States Navy.

5. San Diego is home to 7,000 farms, the most of any city in the United States.

6. May 29 is Tony Hawk Day in San Diego.

7. San Diego has the most dog-friendly restaurants of any city in the United States.

8. The movie *Top Gun* was filmed in multiple San Diego County locations.

9. San Diego is one of only two places in the world where the rare Torrey Pine trees grow.

10. The average temperature in San Diego is a perfect 70 degrees.

CHAPTER 17:

WINNY

QUIZ TIME!

1. During his 22-season MLB career, Dave Winfield played for the San Diego Padres, Minnesota Twins, California Angels, Cleveland Indians, Toronto Blue Jays, and what other team?

    a. Los Angeles Dodgers

    b. Baltimore Orioles

    c. St. Louis Cardinals

    d. New York Yankees

2. Dave Winfield was born on October 3, 1951.

    a. True

    b. False

3. Where was Dave Winfield born?

    a. Baltimore, Maryland

    b. St. Paul, Minnesota

    c. Chicago, Illinois

    d. Atlanta, Georgia

4. How many All-Star Games was Dave Winfield named to during his 22-season MLB career?

    a. 12

    b. 14

    c. 16

    d. 18

5. Dave Winfield's full name is David Mark Winfield.

    a. True

    b. False

6. How many World Series championships did Dave Winfield win in his 22-season MLB career?

    a. 0

    b. 1

    c. 2

    d. 3

7. How many Gold Glove Awards did Dave Winfield win?

    a. 3

    b. 5

    c. 7

    d. 9

8. Dave Winfield's career batting average is .283.

    a. True

    b. False

9. How many Silver Slugger Awards did Dave Winfield win?

a. 2

b. 4

c. 6

d. 8

10. What year was Dave Winfield inducted into the National Baseball Hall of Fame?

a. 2000

b. 2001

c. 2002

d. 2003

11. What season did Dave Winfield lead the National League in RBIs?

a. 1977

b. 1978

c. 1979

d. 1980

12. Dave Winfield stole 223 bases in his career.

a. True

b. False

13. How many home runs did Dave Winfield hit?

a. 305

b. 365

c. 405

d. 465

14. During the 1994 MLB strike, Dave Winfield appeared on an episode of *Married with Children*.

a. True

b. False

15. How many hits did Dave Winfield collect?

   a. 2,910

   b. 3,010

   c. 3,110

   d. 3, 210

16. How many RBI did Dave Winfield collect?

   a. 1,733

   b. 1,833

   c. 1,933

   d. 2,033

17. Dave Winfield was given a full basketball scholarship to the University of Minnesota.

   a. True

   b. False

18. Which NBA team drafted Dave Winfield?

   a. Dallas Mavericks

   b. Minnesota Timberwolves

   c. Los Angeles Lakers

   d. Atlanta Hawks

19. Which NFL team drafted Dave Winfield (even though he never played college football)?

   a. San Diego Chargers

   b. Minnesota Vikings

c. New York Giants

d. Atlanta Falcons

20. In 2004, Dave Winfield was named the third best all-around athlete of all time in any sport by ESPN.

a. True

b. False

QUIZ ANSWERS

1. D – New York Yankees

2. A – True

3. B – St. Paul, Minnesota

4. A – 12

5. A – True

6. B – 1

7. C – 7

8. A – True

9. C – 6

10. B – 2001

11. C – 1979

12. A – True

13. D – 465

14. A – True

15. C – 3,110

16. B – 1,833

17. A – True

18. D – Atlanta Hawks

19. B – Minnesota Vikings

20. A – True

DID YOU KNOW?

1. Dave Winfield is one of only six players to be drafted by teams in three different professional sports leagues.

2. From 2001 to 2013, Dave Winfield was an executive vice president and senior adviser for the San Diego Padres.

3. Dave Winfield was the first active athlete to create a charity foundation.

4. Dave Winfield was inducted into the National College Baseball Hall of Fame in 2006.

5. Dave Winfield made his MLB debut at 21 years old against the Houston Astros. He played in his final MLB game at 43 years old against the Kansas City Royals.

6. Winfield was originally drafted by the Baltimore Orioles out of high school. He was drafted by the Padres four years later.

7. Dave Winfield is a member of the San Diego Padres Hall of Fame.

8. Dave Winfield had the winning hit in the 1992 World Series with the Toronto Blue Jays.

9. At 41 years old, Dave Winfield became the third-oldest player to hit an extra base hit in the World Series.

10. Dave Winfield was the first player to be inducted into the National Baseball Hall of Fame with a San Diego Padres hat depicted on his plaque.

CHAPTER 18:

PEAVY

QUIZ TIME!

1. What is Jake Peavy's full name?

   a. Jacob Paul Peavy

   b. Paul Jacob Peavy

   c. Edward Jacob Peavy

   d. Jacob Edward Peavy

2. Jake Peavy spent his entire 15-season MLB career with the San Diego Padres.

   a. True

   b. False

3. Where was Jake Peavy born?

   a. St. Paul, Minnesota

   b. Mobile, Alabama

   c. Cleveland, Ohio

   d. Tampa, Florida

4. How many All-Star Games was Jake Peavy named to in his 15-season MLB career?

a. 1

b. 3

c. 5

d. 7

5. How many World Series championships did Jake Peavy win?

    a. 0

    b. 1

    c. 2

    d. 3

6. How old was Jake Peavy when he made his MLB debut?

    a. 19

    b. 20

    c. 21

    d. 22

7. Jake Peavy is one of seven players in MLB history to win back-to-back World Series championships with two different teams.

    a. True

    b. False

8. How many Cy Young Awards did Jake Peavy win?

    a. 1

    b. 2

    c. 3

    d. 4

9. What year did Jake Peavy win the National League pitching Triple Crown?

   a. 2005
   b. 2006
   c. 2007
   d. 2008

10. How many times did Jake Peavy lead the NL in strikeouts?

   a. 1
   b. 2
   c. 3
   d. 4

11. In which year did Jake Peavy lead the NL in wins?

   a. 2004
   b. 2005
   c. 2006
   d. 2007

12. Jake Peavy was the MLB ERA leader in 2004 and 2007.

   a. True
   b. False

13. How many Gold Glove Awards did Jake Peavy win?

   a. 0
   b. 1
   c. 2
   d. 3

14. What is Jake Peavy's career ERA?

    a. 3.03
    b. 3.23
    c. 3.43
    d. 3.63

15. How many strikeouts did Jake Peavy collect?

    a. 2,007
    b. 2,107
    c. 2,207
    d. 2,307

16. Jake Peavy was born on May 31, 1981.

    a. True
    b. False

17. How many times was Jake Peavy named Pitcher of the Month?

    a. 0
    b. 1
    c. 3
    d. 5

18. How many times was Jake Peavy named Pitcher of the Week?

    a. 1
    b. 2
    c. 3
    d. 4

19. What year did Jake Peavy make his MLB debut with the San Diego Padres?

   a. 2000
   b. 2001
   c. 2002
   d. 2003

20. Jake Peavy's career win-loss record is 152-126.

   a. True
   b. False

QUIZ ANSWERS

1. D – Jacob Edward Peavy

2. B – False (He pitched for the Padres, Chicago White Sox, San Francisco Giants, and Boston Red Sox.)

3. B – Mobile, Alabama

4. B – 3

5. C – 2

6. C – 21

7. A – True

8. A – 1

9. C – 2007

10. B – 2

11. D – 2007

12. A – True

13. B – 1

14. D – 3.63

15. C – 2,207

16. A – True

17. D – 5

18. B – 2

19. C – 2002

20. A – True

DID YOU KNOW?

1. Jake Peavy made his MLB debut with the San Diego Padres against the New York Yankees. He played in his final MLB game with the San Francisco Giants against the Los Angeles Dodgers.

2. Jake Peavy was the starting pitcher for the National League in the 2007 All-Star Game.

3. Jake Peavy holds the San Diego Padres records for most career strikeouts and most strikeouts in a single game.

4. Without corrective lenses, Jake Peavy is considered legally blind.

5. Even though he did not attend college, Jake Peavy is a fan of the Alabama Crimson Tide football team.

6. Jake Peavy has been a smokeless tobacco user since he was in the fifth grade.

7. Jake Peavy learned to play guitar in 2002 while a teammate of Tim Flannery.

8. Jake Peavy suffered a broken rib while celebrating the Padres' 2005 National League West championship.

9. Jake Peavy was captain of Team USA in the 2006 World Baseball Classic, which took place in San Diego.

10. Jake Peavy is one of only two starting pitchers to win back-to-back World Series championships with two different teams.

CHAPTER 19:

AMERICA'S PASTIME

QUIZ TIME!

1. How many total teams play in Major League Baseball?

    a. 15

    b. 20

    c. 30

    d. 33

2. Major League Baseball was founded in 1903.

    a. True

    b. False

3. Who is the current commissioner of Major League Baseball?

    a. Bart Giamatti

    b. Fay Vincent

    c. Bud Selig

    d. Rob Manfred

4. What year was the National League founded?

a. 1870

b. 1876

c. 1903

d. 1911

5. What year was the American League founded?

a. 1888

b. 1901

c. 1903

d. 1918

6. Major League Baseball is the second wealthiest professional sports league. Which league is the wealthiest?

a. NBA

b. NHL

c. NFL

d. MLS

7. MLB headquarters is located in New York City.

a. True

b. False

8. How many games does each MLB team play in a season?

a. 92

b. 122

c. 162

d. 192

9. In which two U.S. states is spring training held?

a. California and Florida

b. Arizona and Florida

c. Arizona and California

d. California and Arizona

10. How many stitches does an MLB baseball have?

a. 98

b. 100

c. 108

d. 110

11. Where is the National Baseball Hall of Fame located?

a. Denver, Colorado

b. Phoenix, Arizona

c. Los Angeles, California

d. Cooperstown, New York

12. All 30 Major League Baseball teams are located in the United States.

a. True

b. False

13. Which is the oldest MLB stadium still in use?

a. Angel Stadium

b. Dodger Stadium

c. Fenway Park

d. Wrigley Field

14. Major League Baseball has the highest attendance of any sports league in the world.

a. True

b. False

15. Fill in the blank: Seventh Inning _____

   a. Jog
   b. Song
   c. Shake
   d. Stretch

16. William Howard Taft was the first United States president to throw out the ceremonial first pitch at a Major League Baseball game.

   a. True
   b. False

17. It is a Major League Baseball rule that all umpires must wear which color underwear in case they rip their pants?

   a. Tan
   b. Gray
   c. White
   d. Black

18. What year did the first Major League Baseball World Series take place?

   a. 1903
   b. 1905
   c. 1915
   d. 1920

19. Former Major League Baseball Commissioner Bart Giamatti is the father of actor Paul Giamatti.

   a. True
   b. False

20. The song traditionally played in the middle of the 7th inning at Major League Baseball games is called *Take Me Out to the Ballpark.*

    a. True
    b. False

QUIZ ANSWERS

1. C – 30

2. A – True

3. D – Rob Manfred

4. B – 1876

5. B – 1901

6. C – NFL

7. A – True

8. C – 162

9. B – Arizona and Florida

10. C – 108

11. D – Cooperstown, New York

12. B – False (The Toronto Blue Jays are located in Canada.)

13. C – Fenway Park

14. A – True

15. D – Stretch

16. A – True

17. D – Black

18. A - 1903

19. A – True

20. B – False (*Take Me Out to the Ballgame*)

DID YOU KNOW?

1. The average lifespan of a ball in a Major League Baseball game is seven pitches. That means that approximately five to six dozen baseballs are used in every game.

2. The Boston Americans won the very first World Series. They defeated the Pittsburgh Pirates in eight games. Today the most games a World Series can go is seven.

3. The New York Yankees currently hold the most World Series titles with 27.

4. Hot dogs are the most popular food item sold at MLB ballparks. Over 21 million hot dogs were sold at MLB stadiums in 2014.

5. The longest Major League Baseball game on record was played on May 9, 1984, between the Chicago White Sox and Milwaukee Brewers. The game lasted 8 hours, 6 minutes. The most innings played in an MLB game was the 26 innings on May 1, 1920, between the Brooklyn Dodgers and Boston Braves.

6. The distance between the pitcher's rubber and home plate distance at MLB ballparks is 60 feet, 6 inches.

7. Before they can be used in a game, each MLB baseball is rubbed with special mud to improve grip and reduce luster. This special mud comes from a specific, secret location in the state of New Jersey.

8. The fastest Major League Baseball game on record took place on September 28, 1919. The game between the New York Giants and Philadelphia Phillies took 51 minutes. An average MLB game is 3 hours.

9. The American League uses a designated hitter, who only hits and does not play in the field. In the National League, the pitcher hits instead of there being a designated hitter. In an interleague game, whether a DH is used or not is determined by which team is the home team. If the home team is from the American League, each team will use a DH. If the home team is from the National League, each team's pitcher will hit.

10. The distance between bases in MLB is 90 feet.

CHAPTER 20:

GOATS

QUIZ TIME!

1. How many World Series championships did Babe Ruth win in his 22-season career?

   a. 3
   b. 5
   c. 7
   d. 9

2. Jackie Robinson's No. 42 was retired by all MLB teams in 1997.

   a. True
   b. False

3. How many All-Star Games was Willie Mays named to in his 22-season MLB career?

   a. 8
   b. 14
   c. 20
   d. 24

4. How many National League batting titles did Tony Gwynn win in his 20-season MLB career?

   a. 2
   b. 6
   c. 8
   d. 10

5. Rickey Henderson holds the all-time MLB record for most stolen bases. How many did Rickey steal in his 25-season MLB career?

   a. 1,306
   b. 1,406
   c. 1,506
   d. 1,606

6. What year was Hank Aaron inducted into the National Baseball Hall of Fame?

   a. 1980
   b. 1981
   c. 1982
   d. 1983

7. Derek Jeter was named the 1996 American League Rookie of the Year.

   a. True
   b. False

8. How many Gold Glove Awards did Ken Griffey Jr. win in his 22-season MLB career?

a. 7

b. 8

c. 9

d. 10

9. How many no-hitters did Nolan Ryan throw during his 27-season MLB career?

   a. 1

   b. 3

   c. 7

   d. 9

10. Ted Williams missed which season(s) due to military service?

    a. 1943

    b. 1944

    c. 1945

    d. All of the above

11. How many times was Joe DiMaggio named MVP in his 13-season career?

    a. 0

    b. 1

    c. 2

    d. 3

12. Stan Musial spent his entire 22-season MLB career with the St. Louis Cardinals.

    a. True

    b. False

13. What year was Reggie Jackson inducted into the National Baseball Hall of Fame?

   a. 1990
   b. 1993
   c. 1995
   d. 1999

14. Cal Ripken Jr. spent his entire 21-season MLB career with the Baltimore Orioles.

   a. True
   b. False

15. How many All-Star Games was Roberto Clemente named to in his 18-season MLB career?

   a. 5
   b. 10
   c. 15
   d. 18

16. Johnny Bench spent his entire 17-season MLB career with the Cincinnati Reds.

   a. True
   b. False

17. How many times did Sandy Koufax lead the league in ERA in his 12-season MLB career?

   a. 2
   b. 3
   c. 4
   d. 5

18. In which year was Frank Robinson named the National League Rookie of the Year?

    a. 1955
    b. 1956
    c. 1965
    d. 1966

19. Lou Gehrig spent his entire 17-season career with the New York Yankees.

    a. True
    b. False

20. Rod Carew was named the 1967 American League Rookie of the Year.

    a. True
    b. False

QUIZ ANSWERS

1. C – 7

2. A - True

3. D – 24

4. C – 8

5. B – 1,406

6. C – 1982

7. A – True

8. D – 10

9. C – 7

10. D – All of the above

11. D – 3

12. A -True

13. B – 1993

14. A – True

15. C – 15

16. A – True

17. D – 5

18. B – 1956

19. A – True

20. A – True

DID YOU KNOW?

1. Babe Ruth spent his 22-season career with the New York Yankees, Boston Red Sox, and Boston Braves. He is a member of the National Baseball Hall of Fame, the 1923 American League MVP, two-time All-Star, seven-time World Series champion, and 1924 batting champion, and he led the league in ERA in 1916. Ruth is often regarded as the greatest baseball player of all time.

2. Jackie Robinson spent his entire 10-season career with the Brooklyn Dodgers. He is a member of the National Baseball Hall of Fame, the 1949 National League MVP, six-time All-Star, 1955 World Series champion, the 1949 National League batting champion, and 1947 National League Rookie of the Year. Robinson is best known for breaking the color barrier in baseball.

3. Willie Mays spent his 22-season career with the San Francisco Giants and New York Mets. He is a member of the National Baseball Hall of Fame, two-time MVP, 1951 National League Rookie of the Year, 24-time All-Star, 1954 World Series Champion, 12-time Gold Glove Award winner, the 1954 National League batting champion, two-time All-Star Game MVP, and the 1954 Major League Player of the Year.

4. Tony Gwynn spent his entire 20-season career with the San Diego Padres. He is a member of the National

Baseball Hall of Fame, 15-time All-Star, five-time Gold Glove Award winner, seven-time Silver Slugger Award winner, and eight-time batting champion.

5. Rickey Henderson spent his 25-season career with the Oakland A's, New York Yankees, San Diego Padres, New York Mets, Boston Red Sox, Los Angeles Dodgers, Anaheim Angels, Seattle Mariners, and Toronto Blue Jays. He is a member of the National Baseball Hall of Fame, the 1990 American League MVP, two-time All-Star, two-time World Series champion. Henderson is often regarded as the greatest leadoff hitter of all time. He holds the MLB record for most stolen bases.

6. Hank Aaron spent his 23-season career with the Atlanta Braves and Milwaukee Brewers. He is a member of the National Baseball Hall of Fame, the 1957 National League MVP, 25-time All-Star, 1957 World Series champion, two-time NL batting champion, and three-time Gold Glove Award winner.

7. Derek Jeter spent his entire 20-season career with the New York Yankees. He is a member of the National Baseball Hall of Fame, 14-time All-Star, 1996 American League Rookie of the Year, five-time World Series champion, the 2000 World Series MVP, the 2000 All-Star Game MVP, five-time Gold Glove Award winner, and five-time Silver Slugger Award winner.

8. Stan Musial spent his entire 22-season career with the St. Louis Cardinals. He is a member of the National Baseball

Hall of Fame, three-time MVP, 24-time All-Star, three-time World Series champion, seven-time batting champion, and two-time Major League Player of the Year.

9. Cal Ripken Jr. spent his entire 21-season career with the Baltimore Orioles. He is a member of the National Baseball Hall of Fame, two-time MVP, 19-time All-Star, 1982 American League Rookie of the Year, 1983 World Series champion, two-time Gold Glove Award winner, eight-time Silver Slugger Award winner, two-time All-Star Game MVP, and two-time Major League Player of the Year.

10. Sandy Koufax spent his entire 12-season career with the Los Angeles Dodgers. He is a member of the National Baseball Hall of Fame, the 1963 National League MVP, three-time Cy Young Award winner, three-time Triple Crown winner, seven-time All-Star, three-time World Series champion, two-time World Series MVP, five-time National League ERA leader, and two-time Major League Player of the Year.

CONCLUSION

Learn anything new? Now you truly are the ultimate Padres fan! Not only did you learn about the Padres of the modern era, but you also expanded your knowledge back to the early days of the franchise.

You learned about the San Diego Padres' origins and their history, plus about how far they've come. You learned about the history of their uniforms and jersey numbers and read some of the craziest nicknames of all time. You learned more about Mr. Padre, the beloved Tony Gwynn. You also learned about Dave Winfield and Jake Peavy. Plus, who could forget the legendary Trevor Hoffman? You were amazed by Padres stats and recalled some of the most famous Padres trades and drafts/draft picks of all time. You broke down your knowledge by outfielders, infielders, pitchers, and catchers. You looked back on the Padres playoff feats and the awards that came before, after, and during them. You also learned about the Padres' fiercest rivalries both within their division and outside it.

Every team in MLB has a storied history, but the San Diego Padres have one of the most memorable of all. They have gone through winning seasons and losing seasons with the backing of their devoted fans. Being the ultimate Padres fan takes knowledge and a whole lot of patience, which you tested with this book. Whether you knew every answer or were stumped by several questions, you learned some of the most interesting history that the game of baseball has to offer.

The deep history of the San Diego Padres franchise represents what we all love about the game of baseball. The heart, the determination, the tough times, and the unexpected moments, plus the players who inspire us and encourage us to do our best because, even if you get knocked down, there is always another game and another day.

With players like Fernando Tatis Jr., Manny Machado, Eric Hosmer, and Wil Myers, the future of the San Diego Padres continues to look bright. They have a lot to prove but there is no doubt that this franchise will continue to be one of the most competitive teams in Major League Baseball year after year.

It's a new decade, which means there is a clean slate, ready to continue writing the history of the San Diego Padres. The ultimate Padres fan cannot wait to see what's to come for their beloved Friars.

Made in the USA
Las Vegas, NV
03 April 2023

70116253R00095